The Shattered Oak

**Overcoming domestic abuse and
a misdiagnosis of mental illness –
based on a true story**

Sherry Genga

Kristina,

may my words inscribed
on these pages help you
or someone you know not
to feel alone.

all the best.
love. Sherry

The Shattered Oak

Sherry Genga

Copyright ©2019 by Safe Goods

ISBN 9781513644493
Library of Congress Catalog in Publication: 2018967498

Printed in the United States of America
Editor: Nina Anderson
Cover designed by: Kathy Regan

Published by Safe Goods
561 Shunpike Rd.
Sheffield, MA 01257
safe@bcn.net
www.SafeGoodsPublishing.com

Acknowledgements

This book is based on a true story. Although names and facts may have been altered, the true heart of the story beats loudly. Domestic violence and mental instability have torn out the heart of this once happy wife and mother. Desperation, sadness and eventual imprisonment into a mental health facility leads to help for her soul.

My journey to write this book was inspired by a woman named Nina. Thank you for crossing my path. This story would not have been told without you. Also, to my friend Joanne in loving memory, thank you for showing me the gift of reading and the true meaning of friendship. I would like to thank the real Isabelle for being who you are and forever grateful of your kindness.

Lastly, I want to thank my family, my loving husband Jason and my children Justin and Nicole for their support and input. I love you more than words can say.

What readers say.

"This is an excellent book. Learning in school and training in residency may not always lead to the correct answer. We, as physicians, must always question that the obvious answer may not be correct. Medicine is a career of learning, unlearning, and learning anew as new diseases and cures are discovered. We should never avoid questioning a diagnosis or treatment as was well demonstrated by this book."

-Mark Tuttle, MD

Table of Contents

Illustration by Sam Lee Staubach
Facebook page: Sam Lee /Mazoku Designs

Chapter 1

Survival 1975

As the first fist hits my face, one strike after another, the impact is too strong for a cry as my eyes begin to swell. I am unable to cry. Why God? Why God? Why do I deserve this? Why does my flesh and blood hurt so much? Why are my bones aching? Please help me. Somebody help me, rescue me please — but there's no one there. No one to answer my cries. My tears finally start rolling down my cheek bones. My heart is in complete sadness. I'm all alone and desperate to get away from these penetrating, hurting, fast, strong knuckles striking my face. One blow after another, with the pain so strong I feel numb inside. My face feels like that of a boxer's punching bag being hit repeatedly. The blows come fast, strong and furious. My head hits the floor. I hear no sound. This boxer, the man I call my husband, leaves me helpless on the cold floor. I become unconscious and feel left behind. My bruises turn into welts and my cuts bleed slowly from my face. Initially my welts look like bee stings, but within minutes they turn into tiny golf balls. With battle scars embedded on my face from repeated attacks, my face looks like a war zone.

My attacker, my knight in shining armor, the man I married is gone for now. In a fury and rage, he leaves the house, jumps in his car and erratically speeds away. There is now a moment of quiet and peace in the house. I am asleep, drifting in the heavens in peace where I feel no pain. I have been once again knocked around. This life of marriage is no savior from my past. My husband does not embrace me. He rejects me.

There is no fairy tale in this log building. This wood house is not what I call home. It may be made from strong crafted timbers, but on the inside, it is dark, cold, and damp. It has such an eerie feel, as if Satan is lurking in the shadows. The hairs on my arms stand up straight enhancing the fear generated in the darkness. Our log house is set on a private secluded lot on a mountain with a breathtaking view being framed by a proud oak tree.

We live in a two-story rustic log house with a three-car garage, doors painted brown. Attached is a large covered front porch decorated like a living room. On one end of the porch is a large wooden swing. I spend hours daydreaming in that wooden cradle. Here I can rock away some of my fears and enjoy comfort like a baby wrapped up in a swaddle, tight and secure. At the other end is a chaise lounge and two wooden chairs with green and white plaid cushions.

Inside the house are three upstairs bedrooms—one for each of my children. The oldest is Mary, a teenager who gives me joy especially when she plays the flute in the marching band at school. Isabelle, who will become a teenager next year, is my softball star. She recently made Captain and inspires me with her skill and determination. And my youngest is Sara who is a robust combination of the two siblings. She performs in the school band and is a competitive athlete following in the footsteps of her two older sisters.

Our first floor has a modest kitchen, white laminate counter tops, and a stainless-steel sink placed in the center island. The walls are decorated with fruit motif vinyl wallpaper with dark wooden oak cabinets. The appliances are green like the color of peas. Our master bedroom is down the hall away from the rest of the house. It looks as pretty as a garden with pink flowered wall paper and rose color carpet. This oversized room is so large it has two entrances, one at each end.

The living room is grand with tall cathedral ceilings. Plenty of windows are placed around the room, bringing in the day's sunlight. At the end of the room there is a small window placed up high near the peak of the roof. The window was installed there for a loft we never built. I decided to place stain glass over the unused window. It filters in the array of pretty colors that cascade down with the waning sun and reminds me of the magnificent church windows that bring in rays of hope during our Sunday morning mass.

At the other end of the living room there is a fieldstone fireplace, with its stoic rocks standing tall from floor to ceiling that are interrupted only by a beautiful wood mantel and a blue slate hearth for seating. The wall to wall shag carpeting matches the colors in the fieldstone. Directly in the middle of the room is a wagon wheel light fixture, hanging by a black iron chain from one of three large decorative beams that run horizontally and helps to give the room a rustic appearance.

Our yard is covered mostly with sand and green crab grass. Flowerbeds surround the edges of the grass. Orange tiger lilies, bleeding heart, honeysuckle and rose bushes bloom in the summer months to create a harmonious smell. Our wonderful stoic oak tree shades the impatiens with their multiple red and white blossoms flowing like a carpet beneath it. On the side of our garage we hide our large RV. Tall wild grass covers the tires, as it hasn't moved in the last few years.

In the front of the house is a natural stone walkway leading to the front door. Off to the side of the walkway is a flowerbed with green spruce bushes. Placed in the middle of the flowerbed is a tall metal white flag pole, that often hosts our American flag. I take full ownership, pride and responsibility for caring for the flag. When the heavy rain storms are in the forecast, I draw down on the ropes, detach the clips and carry the American flag inside. I iron the flag if needed, then fold it perfectly square and place it in a plastic bin until the storm passes.

An abundance of pine trees shades the woods that surround our yard. The large and strong ones capture the sunlight with sap dripping slowly from their core. Pine cones dangle from their extended branches, the wind carries the natural sent of pine needles. Barn owls and snow owls "hoot" in the forest, as they are building their home for the months to come.

The years pass, my children grow taller and the beatings continue. My once proud and vibrant oak tree senses my pain. I am connected to this old majestic tree that recently was struck by lightning. As I am dying inside from the fear of the next beating, the tall oak tree also suffers in fear of the next blow from Mother Nature. Now standing like a solitary soldier with moss growing at the base of the bark, many of its branches are now bare and lifeless. Its broken branches are hanging on trying to survive —dangling and not wanting to break apart like the bones in my body. This old oak tree is trying to stay together all in one piece yet dying from the inside out. It has few green leaves with little oxygen flowing and some branches devoid of any signs of life.

This is the same feeling I get when my husband makes me have relations with him, holding my wrists, laying on top of me, giving me no choice. Like the oak, I feel I am dying from the inside out, wanting to scream and shout.

This once thriving big oak tree was so impressively alive and monumental to me. I would spend hours fantasizing under its strong shaded branches. I could stare into space and feel my soul slipping away. My attachment became saddened as I watched this oak slowly deteriorate just like my marriage. Insects are making their home inside this now traumatized oak tree. They march down its grey, dry, branches in a grand parade. A woodpecker sits on the tree's branch. The bird enjoys his morning breakfast, and feels the warmth of the rising, orange-yellow sun, that crests above the big beautiful pines. The woodpecker fluffs his red fire-engine breast feathers, pecking steady with his long hard beak. He eats the parade of bugs slowly, sucking the life out of these tiny little helpless creatures.

When I awake from my unconsciousness, my children are staring at me with their heads down. They seem amazed, scared and frightened. They wonder what daddy has done again. When will he come back? When will this monster be returning with his evil behavior?

For now, our house is quiet. The children emerge slowly out of their upstairs hiding places, peaking over the railings to see if it is okay. They are scared and shaking from the beatings that occurred just moments ago. They were too afraid to come out when the boxer was striking me. My girls are caring for me once again by placing ice packs on my face. I feel the coldness of the compress on my bruises. My children are reassuring me; they tell me it's going to be okay. Somehow our roles as parent and child are reversed. It's not I, a mother who takes care of my children, but my children who nurture me back to health. They spoon feed me by filling my mouth with puréed baby food, spoon after spoon. I am too weak to care, and my face is too swollen. For the moment, everyone is scared and frightened of this demon in our house.

The children's father can be loving and caring when he is not drinking his whiskey. The choice is his, and his only. His temper flips like a switch when his bipolar personality emerges. When the switch is turned on he is the meanest. His strength is like an ox and his temper irrational. He is like an unpredictable rumbling bull. This man has a gun collection, stored in our bedroom and is unafraid to use them. These guns hunt and kill the helpless animals who run free in the wild, not knowing if there is a killer stalking them.

In our living room my husband has deer heads mounted and nailed to our log walls. Their preserved heads hanging like a trophy or a first-place blue ribbon. A bear lies on the floor, its eyes and claws glossed over with clear paint, bullet holes hidden in the fur. This proud bear, turned into a rug sprawled out flat on the living room floor, is one more trophy for a man who is proud that he has conquered the defenseless animals who live peacefully in the darkness of the forest. This is a man who uses his muscles to hurt the weak. He preys on those he can control. He is unhappy with his life and unaware of his own anger disorder. The father of my children directs verbal and physical abuse towards me in order to release the anger and pain that festers within him from his childhood.

Chapter 2

Innocent 1943

My husband's childhood lacked nurturing from his mother and father. Joseph, his father, was a raging alcoholic, too drunk to be a provider. He chose to live on the edge of poverty. His mother, Julia, hid behind her alcoholic husband. She was afraid of her own shadow due to his abuse. Joseph was a preacher and was so devoted to God that he named his own son Innocent from the Bible. Ironically, Innocent (that word is used in the bible for purity, goodness, righteousness, saintliness, honor, integrity, decency) was far from a perfect name for my undiagnosed bipolar and abusive husband.

Innocent had to grow up fast. He had to learn to be independent and think for himself. In order to survive poverty, he became street smart. Education was not important. What was important is that he learned the skills of survival. Innocent had his own struggles in life. Food was scarce for his family. They existed on only what the state check allowed. Most of the money went for booze. Many times, Innocent had to go to bed hungry without dinner. Often there was no food in the cupboards and obviously no warm baked apple pies in the oven for dessert. With only bare essentials in the kitchen for food, Innocent usually grabbed raw potatoes to eat, in order to belay the night's hunger pains. After dinner his mother never tucked him in at night. There were no words like "I love you" or "I am proud of you" coming from his mom.

To keep warm, Innocent only had worn out old blankets with holes that lay across his bed. Broken windows by his side let the cold winter air in. Many things were missing from their old white colonial farm house set up on the hills. There wasn't a furnace for heat nor pipes for running water like most of the other houses in town. Since no bathrooms or toilets were installed in the house, he had to use the outhouse which was in a small wooden shed. Trudging through the rain in summer or the blistering winds and heavy snow of winter he made his way to the shed that had a wooden seat covering a pungent deep dark hole.

As a young child, Innocent had the job of providing water for the house. He had to take his empty buckets across the dirt road, over a small wooden bridge and then walk down the embankment to the river's edge. His mother used those buckets of water for cooking, cleaning and the weekly baths. He would have to scoop his buckets in the cold rapid water collecting as much as he could. After he was done filling them up he would have to carry the heavy buckets back up the river bank, trying not to spill a drop. Passing over the bridge and back to the dirt road, he would slowly make his way to the yard with his tired muscles burning and aching. Just wanting to drop the heavy buckets of water, he always made it home from his long journeys. Juggling the buckets, he would turn the knob and successfully open the old, weathered front door that showed years of wear from the heavy rain and snow in the cold northern town of Altoona, Pennsylvania.

Like any child Innocent had a dream of his own, which was to get a blue bicycle with a black stitched seat. He imagined shiny chrome rims with spokes. He found excitement in his dream as he pedaled fast down that dirt road, with the wind hitting his face from the accelerated speed while exploring the wonders of the land. Innocent knew very well that his family had no money for a bicycle as there were no luxury items in his home. He had no new clothes to wear or toys to play with. His shoes were so old the soles were falling apart, flapping when he ran and even making him trip at times. To solve that problem, he would wrap tape around the front of his shoe closing the gap up tight, so he could run and jump without ever falling.

Innocent knew of one place he could go to find some left over toys or broken bikes. These items may have been scratched or broken, but they were like valuable gems to him. To salvage these left-behind treasures, he would walk three miles down the dirt road to the local town dump. To get in he had to climb over a steel gate. To him, this junk yard was the equivalent of a local department store, but without a price tag. It was a treasured place for a poor child who felt like a pirate finding gold. It took Innocent many trips to find all the parts for his bicycle. On the first trip he found two pedals and the frame of an old rusty bike. After a few more trips he managed to find a handle bar, bald tires and then a chain. Then learned how to construct and build his first bicycle.

The color was red and with many spots of brown rust that revealed its abandoned history. Rims were dim and weathered with uneven raised metal like sandpaper showing their age. The seat was ripped with little foam cushioning, but he made a working, riding, pedaling machine. He was very proud of completing this task done without any support from his dad. His skill in building, creating, constructing and putting together mechanical things was in his blood. He showed signs of becoming a mechanical genius. His calloused hands were born to be a tool and they provide a lifeline for his success. He was a young boy preparing himself for prosperity and confidence in the future, but for now he was just a poor child living in the country hills of Pennsylvania.

Innocent had six other siblings in his family. All their names were chosen from the bible. There were five boys, and one sister Mary, who was born with extreme special needs. His father was very ashamed of Mary. After she was born at the hospital, Joseph told Julia he would be sending their new born baby girl away. He knew that they would not be able to provide and care for her. Julia was devastated and sickened from grief. This baby was her only daughter. The State of Pennsylvania was awarded custody of Mary after her birth and became her provider for the rest of her life. Innocent and all of his brothers were prohibited to ever speak a word or talk about their sister Mary again. Silenced forever, Mary had to be forgotten.

Innocent had no escape. He had to share, live and exhibit respect in the same house as his alcoholic father and figure out his own way to survive. Joseph was a tall man with a stern voice. He had an incredible memory. When Joseph was drunk, he would preach, babble and curse repeating the scriptures from the bible to his family, word for word. His drinking got in the way of being a good father. On-the-wagon and then off-the-wagon, his life was like the wheels on Innocent's bicycle going around and around and never escaping the viscous circle. Every day was a different outcome and like Innocent's bike rides, some paths were smooth, some were rocky. You never knew what you were going to get. Even Julia, who tried to care for her children the best she knew how, stayed quiet and turned a blind eye. She lived and obeyed her husband's words. The family survived by accepting state assistance.

Innocent was nicknamed "Inny" as a child. He got teased, harassed and was picked on in school for that unique name. In order to get away from poverty and his family, shortly after his seventeenth birthday he joined the Armed forces. It was an escape from home, childhood and the past. He was leaving the small town of Altoona, Pennsylvania and moving to Virginia with the military.

Innocent was unaware that as a minor, when your family is on welfare, you were financially required to send a portion of your paycheck to your parents. Sending money home to help support his siblings and his drunken father did not sit well for Innocent. His earnings were garnished for a year until he reached legal age as an adult. Joseph once again would spend most of the money on booze. Innocent became extremely resentful of his father. After he turned the age of eighteen, he cut off all ties with his parents and never looked back.

It is hard to give love if you have never been loved. Innocent struggled with the demons of his childhood and carried this burden forward by releasing his anger on his family.

Chapter 3

Divorce 1976

Innocent did provide a respectable living for our family, even somewhat generously. We went on family day trips to amusement parks or mini vacations to airshows. We enjoyed the antics of the stunt planes. Innocent watched these intently because he was a recreational pilot too.

Every summer we would take long road trips to different states. On one of these trips we traveled to Wyoming and Yellowstone Park. Inside the national park we saw beautiful Old Faithful with its natural springs. There were huge waterfalls flowing from the red rocks in the valley, and we saw wild elk that roamed the landscape crossing the busy roads. We were in awe of the picture-perfect scenery.

The following year we all drove to Virginia Beach to frolic in the surf. When we walked down to the busy oceanfront boardwalk we were in awe of the many different vendors and amusement rides. The girls were delighted and didn't want to leave.

On both trips we traveled in our RV. Innocent built our mobile home from scratch doing all the work himself. It was a nice size camper with white siding and a brown stripe. There was a steel ladder attached to the back near the bumper reaching to the roof. We even had an air conditioner for those hot summer nights. The inside of the camper was not your typical luxury motorhome. The RV was an empty box inside. An open shell. We had electricity but no facilities. It was furnished with wall to wall carpet and two captain chairs in front. We had one queen bed in the rear of the camper. The girls slept in sleeping bags. The children enjoyed how big and spacious it was inside. There was so much space they could walk, run and play.

We would play card games during the day, Crazy Eights, War or Spit. Sometimes as a family we would play the license plate game using the alphabet to pass the time until we reached our destination. We all enjoyed our family vacations together.

The earlier years were more tolerable than the later years of this seventeen-year marriage. We would dine out at popular family restaurants at least once a week. The kid's favorite place to eat was Ponderosa, a cafeteria style, self-serve restaurant. Sometimes we would go shopping at the mall or take the children to a popular movie. We appeared to be a typical middle-class family.

My girls looked up to their father. They knew how incredibly smart he was. Innocent described himself by saying, "If you are 'street smart' you don't have to be book smart to be successful." He would say things like, "your father did it, I am a king, I'm the best Dad!" Their father was a natural great story teller. Oh, how the kids would listen to his talks. Innocent would say to them, "always think positively, stop that negative talk and you can do anything you put your mind to if you work hard enough just like Dad." You couldn't help but be captivated by his re-markable preaching. He must have inherited that talent from his own father, listening to Joseph preach. We all would all listen with open ears to Innocent's motivational speeches. All the kids adored that part of their father. Innocent added comedy and humor to his stories. You would listen and laugh all at the same time enjoying his conversation. When he spoke, everyone in the room would stop and listen because he was so captivating.

God, was he handsome and attractive when he preached. We all loved him in those remarkable moments. My heart is torn in half when I think of Innocent, half loving him and the other half fearing for my life.

After the military, Innocent became a very successful business man. At a young age he became an equal partner in a local auto repair shop, C&I. He worked hard, often well into the night to reach his goal of becoming a cornerstone of the automotive industry. After several years, C&I became the largest repair chain in the state. The C stands for Carl, his partner. Senior in years, Carl had years of experience as a mechanic and business owner. He was a father figure and a true best friend for Innocent. Profits were booming and the money was pouring in.

Eventually Innocent had to buy the business from Carl, not by choice. Carl was physically getting too old to keep up in this fast-paced competitive industry. Innocent kept the original name of the business. He was grateful and appreciated his partner for being a great teacher and a mentor.

After Innocent legally became the sole owner of C&I, he decided to have a grand opening at his new location. It was double in size and assured success. His million-dollar company was thriving. The goal he set had been realized. The employees and customers assumed that he was happily married with three beautiful girls. Innocent wanted to maintain this perfect image, so he insisted that the family members keep everything private; (i.e. don't talk outside the house.) He was emphatic when he said, "never let anyone know what's going on, privacy is a must! Privacy, privacy, keep everything private. Nothing leaves this house, not now, not ever. Family business is nobody else's. Keep your mouth shut Barbara, or I will shut it for you. Don't tell a soul." Everything had to be a secret!

In the evening, within the darkness of my home, I cleaned the house, cooked and made sure everything was perfect for my husband when he came home. Dinner was in the oven, set on warm, waiting for him. And I was waiting— scared, for I was never sure what kind of mood he would stroll in with. Will I be subject to his good mood or bad mood? Will he arrive at midnight or dinner time? These questions ran through my mind. Is he going to yell and scream at me, tell me I'm worthless? Will there be physical abuse? Will he take it out on the kids or just me? Will he just go to his room and pass out from drinking too much whiskey? Will he force me to have sex—hard, painful, unreasonable sex? Is he going to tell me again that he is going to kill me? Or will he go crazy once again and grab a gun, point it straight at me using his pointer finger to pull the trigger missing me on purpose at the last second, and lodging a bullet hole in my kitchen wall.

More than once I was left to patch the holes with the same matching fruit wallpaper or leave them there as a painful reminder. Will he try and shoot again, not missing this time and blow me away? Will he take out the distributor wires in my car and remove the spark plugs? This has become a habitual task done regularly after my beatings, intended to leave me stranded with no way to escape.

Will he abuse me till I'm black and blue, while I am praying for God to help me? Will this violence continue even when I'm trying in desperation to dial the phone—bleeding, shaking, frantic, hyperventilating, pressing each number to call 911, praying to God once again for some relief? Will Innocent, manipulate the phone away from my ear, yank the phone jack right out of the wall and throw it to the ground? Will he smash it in pieces with the metal mechanisms inside the phone hanging and swaying like a pendent? There is never any help—no cops—I'm always dying of fear within my own skin.

My brother, my sister, and even my mother, won't help me. They are terrified of my husband. They do not want to interfere or get involved with my marriage or me. They all dread he would come after them. They desert me because they are fearful and afraid, not offering any help. I have no family or friends to hear my sobs or my prayers. My husband forbids me to have any close friendships as it is not allowed.

I am so alone…I am so scared not just for myself, but for my three children. My anxiety is rising. I'm having panic attacks.

When will I see those headlights in my driveway—the beams of fright approaching? These lights are not from heaven. They are lights of fire, yellow and orange lights, from hell. Those headlights petrify me as they approach up the hill, cresting my turnaround, the large dirt circle in front of the house. I am hearing the car tires hit the gravel right in front of the garage.

If I pray hard enough with my rosary beads will I be saved by the cops? Will they make him leave? Will the troopers wait for one night at the end of the driveway, so he can no longer hurt me? Will there ever be an arrest, jail time, or consequences for him hurting me. Will I escape tonight? Will I be able to drive my children to a hotel room for our safety? I could head for a dirty, old room, cheap enough for me to afford a safe night sleep. For our one-night escapes I would use my hidden money, two twenty-dollar bills, that I keep in the rubber backing of the car's rear-view mirror.

No words in the English dictionary could describe how frightened I have become. I am terrified and scared as a tiny, small mouse, wishing I had somewhere to hide—a secret place where I will not be harmed, a safe haven. Safe? There is no safe place!

The years pass in my marriage and laws change in the state of Connecticut. Women now receive more rights. Husbands have to pay for their actions in domestic violence or get arrested. The abuse is still prevalent in my life, but divorce is very hard to fathom.

Innocent starts finding his satisfaction other places. He doesn't always make it home every night like he used to. When it comes to women he is a formidable player —attractive, lean, 6'4", hazel eyes and dark jet-black hair with a muscular physique. Innocent rarely goes out without wearing his aviator glasses, hiding the truth behind his eyes. He is good at showing off, talking and flirting with women he meets in a bar. He brags about being a pilot and a successful business owner. He is a lady's man who knows how to swindle women. Good looking and a smooth talker, Innocent is blessed with money and success.

Innocent has many affairs throughout our marriage, one-night stands and girls he meets at the bars after leaving me bruised and bleeding on the kitchen floor. I often mentioned to him that I was aware that he was having affairs with other women. I accused him of having a Bobby pin in his pocket, lipstick stains on his shirts or long hairs on his clothing that didn't match mine. The more I accused him, the more I got abused and the more I became silent.

In our last year of marriage, I finally I got brave and decided to let him know I didn't want to share our bedroom. I put up a divider that hung from the ceiling in the middle of the room. I bought a small twin bed and placed a flowered comforter on top. One large picture of a waterfall made from cardboard displayed for tranquility hung on my wall. This was a tiny little space that was just for me. I envisioned that I could finally stretch out and relax in my own bed and I didn't need to wonder about him anymore. I let myself be separated. I was adjacent to him but felt detached in this marriage.

Alone at night in my tiny space I never felt safe. In the middle of the night I could hear his breathing. We are both sleeping in this large bedroom with only a flimsy canvas wall dividing us that gave me only limited relief from the fear. He shouted at me and even threatened my life, but he respected my wishes to be separated in my private bedroom during the night by keeping his distance.

One night in my little bedroom I had a dream that Innocent was just a ghost and he walked right through the divider to get me. I kept praying that he could not hurt me. Now I rest in my bed with my children asleep. My eyes are closed but my thoughts are running rampant in my mind. When I can't sleep, I open my eyes and turn on the small lamp by my bed. I sit up and place a pillow behind my back.

I reach for my note pad under the bed and find my blue BIC pen. I like to express myself on paper, so I write my thoughts down. My secret journal is where I can write my hopes and fears. As I grasp my pen with its blue ink, I let the words flow on this white-lined paper. I now reveal my deepest darkest thoughts, fears, regrets and wishes. Somehow writing in this journal helps me make sense of my life. I feel like it's therapy for my soul, reassuring me it's okay and helping me through my difficult time. I look forward to these quiet times where I scribble in my journal. Knowing there is a trash can right beside me I can rip up the words describing my dismal state, toss them into the trash and hopefully rid myself of the dark, depressive state that surrounds me. My deepest darkest thoughts from my inner soul are scribed on these pages and help me to become my own therapist. This diary allows me to sort out my situation. I am then able to release my fears and hope for a peaceful future.

My journal is not judgmental, and no one can tell me whether I am right or wrong. No one can correct me. (It's just me alone scripting my own song, my own problems, or my short novel.) Journaling helps me to have closure with my sadness. It helps me figure out what path I should take or how I can change the future to get over this deep dark pain of existence. This blue BIC pen and I scribble words so messy, putting pressure with my fingers applying it to the pen allows my emotions to vent. Sometimes I get so stressed that my writing puts so much pressure on the pen that I make indents deep in the paper. I write about my dark clouds bringing them out of the deep recesses in my memory. Once again there is no judgment as I script my thoughts—crying with tears like rain, telling the truth, trying to be worthy.

When I feel used and neglected, expressing myself makes me feel like there is hope. I need to learn from my mistakes and reflect on that new-found wisdom to change the present. I realize now that I am older, I can choose to make my life better. I just need to find the right support system and summon the courage to go forward.

Finally, I became determined to find a divorce attorney to help me. I had no money to pay. But, a woman lawyer, named Mrs. Hong, offered to help. Her nickname was "Mrs. Hang" because she would defeat and bury her defendant. "Hanged them". That was her reputation. She was a very successful attorney, winning her cases with years of experience and knowing how the court system worked. Her specialty was difficult divorces.

My divorce was complicated considering the business, house, alimony, child support, and the emotional distress I claimed. Mrs. Hong knew she could make a hefty profit from my broken marriage. This domestic case would be a challenge, but money from Innocent's financial success and a myriad of assets would pay for her fees in the settlement, giving the firm a nice profit.

The trial was uncomfortable as I had to discuss and relive those dark days of abuse at the hands of my husband. The court ordered my two older girls, Mary and Isabelle to go on the witness stand. The Judge asked questions about their father; "Was there abuse? How was his character? What happened when your father came home? Did he touch you improperly? "

This was hard for Mary. She was the recipient of many more questions because she was the oldest. Mary was on the witness stand for a long time and faced many difficult questions that she didn't want to answer. Questions about her father put her in a tough spot. Do I tell? Do I make my father unhappy and mad? Mary spoke bravely on the witness stand.

Because of her responses in court, her father never forgave her, nor did he forget. Innocent was outraged by her remarks. He was horrified that she could say "lies" and verbalize such mean things about her father. He never wanted to see her again. He exhibited pure hate for my beautiful child because she spoke the truth by describing what happened behind closed doors. She was now forever disconnected from her father.

When it was Isabelle's turn in court they didn't ask as many hard questions for they knew she was younger and more fragile. She too told the truth. But because her answers did not make her father look like a monster or an unfit dad, her words did not define what kind of person he really was. Still, Innocent was not happy with Isabelle.

The court proceedings were very emotionally draining, disturbing, frustrating, and physically exhausting. It's like reliving a horror movie, uttering scream after scream, and very intense. Mrs. Hong was tough as nails as she pleaded my case. At times, when I was shaking in fright, Mrs. Hong calmed me down by letting me know she was fighting my fight. In her closing remarks about my marriage her words and her actions were effective. This lead the court to decide in my favor.

My divorce was a success. I was awarded child support, alimony, the house, and a lump sum of money from the share from the business. This was to be paid out weekly. I walked out from that court room with my three children by my side. I was free for now, but not free from fright. When I left the court-room and passed by Innocent he stared, silently with his eyes, threatening me with a look of pure hate. It was a look indicating that one day he would still love to keep me silent by taking my breath away, killing me. This made my skin crawl as I kept walking out of the courtroom.

Even with all the tension, I was relieved that day. I uttered a sigh of relief and accomplishment. I am officially divorced, free from Innocent's anger and his bitterness! Because of him I was not the woman I once was. The once-upon-a-time fairy tale had become a violent, decayed marriage. I had called our log domicile a house, but now I can respectfully call it my home. It is now quiet and peaceful. The verbal and physical abuse is just a memory buried within my soul. Now I can release the darkness that enveloped this place. I can shed a new light on a future where I'll be raising my three children, alone.

Chapter 4

Nervous breakdown 1979

I am driving in my gold Oldsmobile Cutlass up the driveway, half a mile from the road and civilization. As I reach the turnaround in the front of the house, I look over and I see my girls' tire swing hanging from the old oak. It's dangling like a thread but, connected with strong yellow nylon rope tightly tied to the dead branch still hanging onto this once magnificent tree. Swaying ever so lightly with the wind blowing, this tire swing takes the rain, snow and wind abuse of Mother Nature, and still the threads are intact. They are not frail and broken like my insides, my mind, so delicate and imbalanced.

After the divorce, I'm not sure what broke inside me. I didn't know it at the time but I was having a nervous breakdown. I thought I would be happy after the divorce, but I was just the opposite. I became severely depressed and full of confused feelings as though I was worthless.

I saw a therapist named Alice once a week. She was an older lady and was like a mother figure to me. Alice had dark black hair with some gray showing around the crown of her face. Tiny wrinkles outlined her tired looking eyes that also revealed a deep inner empathy. She was willing to take on my burdens, listen to my thoughts. She actually seemed concerned about my mental state. Alice was a true gem who embraced her clients' life burdens and took responsibility for people's welfare. Specializing in making sure her clients didn't crack, peel or open a layer of no return, she helped keep them sane. She guided them away from wallowing in their tears of grief. I trusted she would prevent my mind from jumping off the ledge. The scars in my soul were swirling deep in a Grand Canyon-like chasm in my subconscious.

Alice's office was a small room with a brown leather couch, two fluffy red pillows with rich silk curtains draped around a window and a painting of a castle on the wall. A built-in book case traveled the length of the room. Alice's chair was strategically placed in front of a small rounded antique window. In her office, lying on her couch, I always felt like I was stepping into that gold elegant picture frame with a gray castle from medieval times. It depicted two large men in shinny armor suits holding their swords protecting the large wooden doors of this stone castle. Like my dying oak tree that gives me solace, I feel protected when I entered this room.

To help my thoughts flow, she softly dims the lights placed on the end tables. The lamp shades are glowing, casting their shadows next to the tissue boxes. I felt safe enough to reveal my deep and dark, spiral, twisted past. As I lay there, Alice tries to make sense of my story. I begin by opening one of the chambers in my mind. I enter a funnel, the twister in my mind, and talk about my marriage. Alice listens to my trauma like a good therapist does and guides me to a place where I can destroy the evil forces that are still present in my mind.

My depression is slowly engulfing me day by day. It is hard to find the will to get out of bed. Days become weeks and weeks become months. I am lost in my own grief. I lose all my ability to focus on what is important, becoming emotionally drained.

I focus on the medicine prescribed to me for my insomnia. As my hands press down on the lid, turning the white cap with my palms, I open the container and stare down at 100 pills, sleeping pills. This was my loaded gun. Somehow, I thought that things would get better. I reached for my warm glass of water on the night stand. I take handfuls of pills with big gulps of water just trying to end my sorrows. I'm swallowing my pills and my pride. I need to get away. I need to be safe. I want to be in heaven where God loves me.

I hold my rosary beads clutched tightly in my palm. Sweat is forming, as I dig the cross into my hand, the edges sharp, creating indents while I'm squeezing. A man nailed by his palms and feet are in my thoughts. I want to feel his pain, his sacrifice. Blood is pulsing through my veins, hypertension so high I feel my cheeks become red. My heart races. I'm sweating. I see the light from my window simmer across my rosary beads—a light of hope. I say my prayers, apologizing for my marriage and for my choices. As my eyes shed some tears, I put Innocent's picture away. I cannot look at it anymore. My heart is breaking. I need a sacrifice. My sacrifice will be flatlining with no breath, just silence and peace. My complicated past will only be a memory to my children. Oh, I cannot think of them right now. I begin to panic. All I want is freedom. I feel the freedom coming closer—the freedom of being loved and worthy.

I take my last gulp of pills with a warm sip of water touching my lips. My eyes are shutting down; my body is shutting down. Life is withdrawing from my soul. My body is in despair; my spirit, my soul, are looking, searching, for the last time. My eyes are becoming unfocused. The perimeter of my room is blurry. My eye lids are closing and the last thing I see is darkness.

It feels like hours have passed and I am awakening from my darkness. My eyes open slowly. My tear ducts are dry and crusty. I have trouble opening my eyes. My pupils are trying to focus but these lights, these bright, bright lights are blinding. I can't see straight. My eyes are straining, squinting. What is going on? Where am I? I'm so drowsy and tired. Delusional, I lie awake for a few minutes trying to focus. My eyes are starting to adjust. I can see the bright lights even brighter, with big long florescent bulbs running down the ceiling interspersed among the white tiles.

My eyes look down the cement walls, half painted peach the other half painted white. I see bed rails on my bed, long chrome bars to keep me from falling. White sheets are covering my body. I'm tucked tight in bed. I look to my right and I see an IV unit. One bag is hanging with fluid half way full. I follow the tube and see it attached to my arm that is causing constant pain. I look to my left. A big blue machine runs near my bed taking my blood pressure and monitoring the rhythm of my heart. I begin to feel woozy. I look straight ahead. There is a nurse with a white coat on. I can't see her name. I can see her brunette hair in a ponytail, pinned up. She is reading my chart and flipping through the pages on her metal clip board.

I hear the sounds of chaos in the background. People are talking loudly, and some people are screaming in pain. I'm wondering whether I am safe. Did I make it? Or am I dreaming? I start to feel nauseous. My mouth is starting to water. I must be sweating, because I notice that my forehead and my chest are damp. I look over to my left and see my heart rate beating faster on the screen. The machine is beeping louder. There is so much noise echoing off my room walls. My ears are ringing. What is going on with me? I feel so ill. My stomach is burning from the inside. I can feel my insides ready to explode. My body aches. I hear voices, "Barbara, Barbara are you awake? Barbara say something, anything. You're at the hospital." I know that I am listening, but my body functions are slow. I can't react. There is a heavy weight across my body keeping me paralyzed.

I listen to Isabell's loud and scared voice. "Mom please say something. Let me know you are okay." I can barely get the words out but with a soft whisper I answer, "yes, yes". I am ashamed of the weakness in my voice. My daughter, grips my hand holding it tight for dear life. I feel her clench on to my four fingers and my thumb. With tears weeping from the corner of her eyes she whispered, "You scared me. What were you thinking? You can't leave us. Sara and I followed the ambulance here. I drove so fast to keep up, I even ran red lights to follow you here. We need you."

Just as Isabelle was speaking, I start covering my mouth not because of my words but for what is about to come out. I hold my stomach, point with my index finger to the small pink pan placed on my hospital tray. Isabelle grabs it just in time. I start heaving, vomiting like a faucet of water. I wretch so fiercely I over flow the bucket, spilling vomit over the rim and onto my lap. I repeat heaving over and over again with so much pain I thought I would never survive. Is this what I wanted? The nurse with the pony tail tries to comfort my daughters, telling them that the doctors gave me charcoal to make me feel better. The nurse informed Isabelle and Sara that in a few minutes mom will be leaving this room and getting her stomach pumped to force all the pills and medicine out of her system. I think to myself. "Why would I want to leave my children? What is wrong with me? I'm listening to the staff and my surroundings as best I can. How could I be so selfish? I am feeling ashamed that two of my children are by my bedside, watching me as I throw up everything I have. I love my three children. Somebody help me, save me please!" As the warm IV fluids keep running through my veins I realize that I am a survivor of my first suicide attempt not knowing at the time there would be a second and even a third.

Isabelle drove me home the next day from the hospital. I was trying to forgive myself. I was still just in a daze, going through the motions but not mentally there. Our car pulls in front of the garage. As the tires hitting the gravel crunching underneath. I flashed back to the sound that in the past generated fear that vividly replays like a movie in my mind. It is astonishing how the subconscious remembers sounds that connects us to the past.

We get out of the car and Isabelle reaches down for the handle to open the middle garage door. As she opens it, I immediately see my car parked in the same spot as where I left it. I look over to my left and see an empty garage spot with puddles of oil stains translucent on the cement floor. This is the spot that once belonged to Innocent. That garage space still gives me nightmares. Chills run through my body. I walk into the house, one step at a time.

That night I asked the children for forgiveness and pleaded with God to forgive me for my sins. I promised I would talk with Alice and make another appointment for therapy. I told them that I would figure out how I could be a better mother and that I would always be there for them. I admitted my foolishness behavior and assured the kids this would never ever happen again. I was broken and worn down inside but, I asked God for his help. I prayed extra hard during the Sunday morning service and asked the Lord to heal my broken mind.

To bury my sorrows and heal my soul from sadness I listen to music. I enjoy playing my record player. I can look through the clear lid and see the black vinyl record, watching it spin fast like my mind out of control. It goes around and around as the tip of the sharp, metal, pointed needle, finds its place in the grooves. This silver needle, so like the sewing needle that I inserted into the photograph of Innocent's picture, piercing the area of my husband's chest directly through his heart. I carry this picture around with me in my purse. I keep it to remind me of my pain, sadness and broken heart. I listen to my favorite songs spinning on the record, playing out a story to be told. Some are sad songs, some love songs with each verse having a special meaning. The right tune on that old vinyl record never seemed to fit what I was going through. All I can do now is watch the black circular record spin around and play out music that is somebody else's story.

Oh, how I daydream during the day. I drift away and just think. I start dreaming of that old suffering oak tree still standing my backyard. When we moved in the tree was full of life and I took solace under its shade. Now its long fingerling branches show few signs of life. The branches are crooked and bent resembling veins extending out to the moonlit sky, cold and lifeless like my body. I know it would be so easy to disconnect my veins severing them in just one second of time. Using a firm grip holding the sharp razor blade between my thumb and pointer finger I could quickly slice the area where my watch is normally placed. As the blade dug in, I would have seen the steady stream of bright red blood dripping down my wrist turning dark in color as it hits the air. I could just imagine how quickly the blood would drain from my body, emptying my sores, my grief and soul. I would now be cold and alone.

I encompass my thoughts and think of the vibrant color known as red. It is the color of ruby apples so sweet, but the same color of blood, dark, bitter and sour. I would love to take a bite of that poisonous apple and fall into a deep, deep sleep, just like in the fairytale of Snow White. For me, I know there will be no handsome prince to wake me up from this dream. I feel as though I am spiraling down to a point of no return. I daydream silently all alone. Nobody hears my thoughts. I daydream and imagine my death, if I could just apply pressure to my skinny razor blade. Death feels deep, graphic and satisfying for me in my daydreams.

My mind continually acts as a devil's playground—Tasmanian devil. My thoughts are dancing all over the place with the devil himself. I drive down the street from my home to the river. Approaching alongside the river bank I get out of my Oldsmobile and watch the water flow. I know my body is out of control—dislodged, short circuited, haywire. Memories and feelings are racing though my head. Innocent are you happy now knowing that I have been knocked around? God, I used to love you so. My thoughts are jumbled. It's all so obvious now. I look insane. I'm running away from it all. I'm so very alone. It's crazy how I still love you. I know you don't need me, but I hope that you will wish you never did this to me. My thoughts are creating intolerable pressure to do something. I want to reach and touch the sky. I decide to climb the mountainous hill alongside the river.

I walk pass the rapid water and take a small trail that leads up to a cliff overlooking the river. This narrow trail is wrapped with tall skinny trees making me feel trapped, with no way to escape. I see this enclosure as a towering fence squeezing out my inner emotions. I find myself struggling to find fresh air. I finally see a clearing in the dense forest and approach an opening that leads to a massive grey ledge. Most of the rocks are jagged and reaching skyward, resembling a long stairway.

I see this as a path guiding me to the pearly gates of heaven. I give this unique stairway a glance and decide to climb it. Maybe I can find the heavens within the clouds? I manage to walk on this carved uneven path. Gingerly stepping forward, I slowly make it to the top. I am at the flat edge of the ledge. I nudge my chin down trying to keep my balance and see the river flowing below. I feel a dizzy unbalanced sensation. Immediately I look straight ahead lest I fall. A small pebble drops into the water below giving me an idea. I give one quick glance to the sky above. The sun dances behind a cloud giving me deep, dark feelings of desperation. I don't give myself any time to think. I decide to meet my fate.

I know I don't know how to swim, but I jump and release my body. Now free falling I splash into the waters below. I did it. I jumped off the side of a cliff into the deep dark waters below. The weight of my clothing pulls me down. The heaviness of water soaking into my clothing make it hard for me to move. My shoes fill up with water acting like anchor attached to my feet. My arms splash around, but they are like a fishing net skimming the water. My head, barely surfacing, allows me to take small and short breaths. I go down sinking to the bottom. Staying there for a second, I use my feet and push off the rocky bottom and scurry back up to the top. I get to take another frantic breath by leaning my head sideways. With half of my face exposed I choke on some water.

Once again, I am pulled under, fraying my arms and kicking my feet. Sinking again from all the weight, I push off the bottom with all my might and launch myself towards shore. I am giving in to my instinct of survival. My head pops up one more time allowing me to take a breath through my nose and mouth. This time I don't sink beneath the surface. My toes can touch now, like a dancing ballerina tall and thin with my toes extended and my head barely out of water. I tilt my head up to the sky. The sun is shining, white puffy clouds moving over head. I can tippy toe to the left and I start to feel more solid ground as my soles of my shoes are meeting the gravel bottom. My breathing is sporadic and rapid. I take long deep breaths. I am slowly moving my body through the water, walking to the end of the swimming hole. Water levels decrease from my neck to my shoulders, then falling below my knees. I am safe… I ask myself, "Did I honestly want to die? Did I almost leave my three children? Did I genuinely want to survive this episode of submerging in the water? Did I actually want to keep my head afloat?" I pull myself up from the deep dark watery grave and collapse on the side of the river bank, wondering if I had really been saved.

I processed what just happened. Another suicide attempt. I can't believe what I did. I cannot sit around and think of this event. This powerful inhalation of water. I will need to extinguish this memory as fast as I can. I know I went unbelievably white eyed and crazy again. This is undoubtedly not me. I am clearly not thinking straight. I will not have a nervous breakdown! I won't let it happen.

At this moment I need to remind myself of the things that are familiar and endearing to me like the daydreams that keep me sane. This focuses my thinking and makes me stable and strong. The insight, visions and pictures I create in my head keeps me somewhat grounded. Right now I know I am not stable. I am standing on the ground, wobbling, overwhelmed and confused. I think of my old oak tree's roots. The slice of lightning that struck the branch caused part of its roots to remain torn and exposed. They are black and rotten, broken at the core. Its massive branch lays on the ground just waiting to decay. Small shards of fallen bark lay beside the core.

Like the roots I can feel that part of me torn up, ripped apart. I remember myself standing under that old oak tree, knowing it once was a vibrant magnificent specimen of nature. Somehow this old oak tree needs to be pieced back together. It needs a supply of water and nourishment to its fibers. My goal is to stand steadily with two feet together solidly on the ground underneath this old tree. But I know I need time to heal my broken heart.

I run away from this water hole back to my Oldsmobile and place my wet body in the driver's seat. Feeling deflated, worn out and tired, I let out a sigh breathing in and out long and hard. Knowing my judgment is worse than usual, I am compelled to see Alice once again. I need to talk about this irrational behavior. She will take me to my favorite place, my castle in the sky. I can open her office door and enter the gold picture frame on the wall. My daydreams are where I can feel safe. I feel secure in her room, locked and protected. This place is my shield of armor, my gates of heaven. My tragic attempt needs to be shared. I need her for comfort and help to cure my broken mind.

I turn the key and start my car. I look quickly in my rear view mirror and I am sadden what I see. I look so frazzled with my damp, black hair in tangles and mascara running from my face. What has become of me? Why can't I keep it together? Why am I so weak and vulnerable? My reflection is without a doubt out of whack. I ask myself one more time, "Who am I in this reflected mirror? Is this who you want to be?"

I proceeded to drive to Alice's office. I lay there tucked in on her couch feeling the softness of her cushions on my skin with a warm fuzzy blanket wrapped around me. I embrace the tenderness of her smile. She has the knowledge and the strength to get me through this. She will help and support me in dealing with my second attempt at destruction. She will take me to a higher level above the waters where I can breathe. My eyes settle in and I enter the castle on the wall. I stare and focus at the picture as I begin to talk imagining my own inner strength. I am here once again protected, guarded and surrounded by my daydreams in this antique, medieval, castle of a room.

...

Sometime has passed since my two episodes of suicide. For now I close my eyes in my living room and get lost in music. Words that were once written on paper, are now performed in a song for us to hear. I listen mostly to country music. The bass booming loudly from that old black speaker helps me feel the rhythm bouncing through my body. I fantasize about adorning western gear and sporting cowboy boots, kicking my feet up from the ground, putting my hands in the air and surrendering. Not wanting to hear that voice anymore from my past, I try to outrun my thoughts. I can still hear Innocent's raspy, angry, viscous voice that once lived in my house. Now I want to hear the sounds of my favorite country singers, Randy Travis, George Straight and even some Elvis Presley. I can hear their voices echoing off the beams of the rafters in my living room, so my favorite country band will become present and alive within my emotional soul.

In the shadow of my eyes I can get lost in the orchestration of the music. Deep emotion arises inside me when I'm all alone with just the country singer wailing out the song. I will be alone with the stars, the moon and the darkness of the sky. I am feeling the loneliness but still relish dancing in the night. As the sun is setting deeper, I want the music to go through my bones. I can feel the happiness of the notes running through my mind, while the waning sunlight hits my face. I am leaving my unbalanced tilted world tonight. I am learning how to lock it out. My attitude is pronounced and stable as I sing the lyrics to my favorite song.

Minutes later my thoughts become jumbled mixed up in a confused untidy way. This sad song on my speaker produces images that are blurry. Flash backs of my past are here in the present. My mind becomes rampant with random thoughts duplicating a memory of my clothing being removed, not by choice but by force at the mercy of my husband's voracious libido.

I cannot let these images bring me down. I do not want to open that horror again. I need to stop my thinking and find a way to file this vision out of my mind. I cannot help if I wear my feelings on my sleeve. I really am kind, loving, considerate, and companionate. I'm not making any sense in my mind. There are no more hotel suites, no more drunken smirks and smiles. I dance by the TV and I wonder if anybody misses me. I can't get his screams out of my head.

My mind flashes back to those moments of terror. I want to feel invincible, not hearing the words he repeated over and over, "I'll beat you up and never let you go. I will have you craving my attention with every punch that I deliver to your face." I still am afraid. Will he come back and take his anger out on me and the girls? Can divorce really make me safe? Remembering the past, causes my heart to rapidly beat faster.

Right now, I am feeling rage. I am looking to find answers to my unsolved questions. Answers need to be forthcoming on how I ended up in this failed marriage, questions on how I could have made it right and avoided divorce. How could I have helped this man to become less bitter and more loving? My mind is feeling delicate and fragile and in a state of unbalanced insanity. I am scared, and I need to find a way to release this crazy hold on me.

The next day I was very depressed. I needed to take time to clear my head and walk behind my house through our thirty-two acres. This path starts in my back yard and leads to the river. Sometimes I see deer and recently I bought a salt block to attract them. I hung the salt block on my apple tree and now when the deer come to my backyard, I observe these wonderful creatures that to me symbolize a statue of strength. Standing so strong and stout licking the salt block, I marvel at their beauty, their beautiful brown eyes and their striking pose. I consider them one of the most regal animals with their broad white haired chest, strong bodies and antlers stacked so grand.

I treasure these walks. This trail has many grey rocky cliffs and I startle a snake slithering past near the pile of stone. Further up the path I can see dead trees that have fallen down on top of the old stone walls used in the past for cattle and boundary markers. I can dream in this country backyard which is so quiet, serene, smelling of earthy, musty moss among the breeze. There is purity in the air, a word once used for my husband's name. I am still trying to find myself. Still trying to figure out how I can be strong.

My shoulders tense under the weight of all the stress that surrounds me. Cleaning the house, mowing the yard, doing the grocery shopping and all along taking care of the kids is the undercurrent of what keeps me locked up emotionally. I am trying to figure it out the best I know how. I am grateful for my alimony check. There is just enough money to get by and pay the bills. I guess I should feel lucky. I am appreciative that I still have a life to live, but I can't help feeling like I am going down that spiral staircase. Just like descending into my basement with the cold rod iron rails and wooden steps I feel the dampness that surrounds me. This is the same feeling I have in my heavy heart.

I have walked to the end of the trail and meet the river bed. This is where I almost once saw death not that long ago. I admire the river water flowing, swiftly through the rocks with whitecaps forming from the strong undertow. I see its sandy beaches and smell the pungent odor of fish carcasses laying along the shore. I see the water flowing and moving in the right direction. This is the direction I should be going—forward! Sometimes I can see my own body floating down the river as the light reflects and shimmers across the frothing waves. Today I look up and see the blue skies with puffy white clouds. I imagine there is an angel shining down and watching over me.

I am standing by a pool of water created by a dam formed by old trees that took their last breath when felled by a gust of wind during a storm. I glance over at that dam. Water gently flows over the top of it with just enough force. I make sense of this in my head. If my emotions make it over the top, cresting with the same force of energy as the flowing water, it will purge my inner savage beast along the way. Would this curse of mine vanish? Why was I given curse that consumes my life? I give the river one more look, as I continue my walk back home.

I must climb a big hill on my return trek with every step burning the back of my calves and giving my tired body a work out. My arms swinging with my fists in a downward motion to give me power and strength to go uphill. With every stroke, I am pumping them harder and faster to equal the beat of my heart. As I perspire I fantasize about outrunning the demons etched firmly in my mind.

I finally reach my home, taking in the beauty and nature of this picture-perfect house from outside. Stepping up on the front porch I consider resting there for a while. But I choose to open the front door instead. My thoughts are still running wild. As I turn my front door knob I visualize that I am unlocking and opening the door in my mind that is a gateway to my soul. This door is not your average door but the atrium to the space in my heart. My heart is now wide open and feelings of the past push in regardless of my intention to banish them. I walk inside towards my kitchen. The rays of the setting sun reflecting off the cabinets make it hard to see. I open my cupboard and grab a clear drinking glass. My hand is moist from my walk. My hair feels misty from my sweat. I use my other hand to turn the faucet on. Turning the direction of the metal lever to cold, I place my short crystal glass beneath the water. Its gushing force of energy is nothing like the force of nature at the river damn. There the water is slow, smooth and calm as it softly runs across the damn.

I fill my glass half way. All my kids are still at school. I am home alone. I can feel the darkness entering my mind, like a dirty dark thunderstorm cloud being a harbinger of approaching destruction. I can feel the hail storm weighing in my mind. I am starting to fail. I'm not thinking straight.

In my moment of sadness, I make a clear-cut decision with the first sip. The feelings of suicide engulf me. Consequences are a reminder, but my shoulders are getting heavy and my lungs are taking small breaths. Once again, I am suffocating within my own body. I am moving but I'm not sure where I will end up. I stop for a second. I am so scared. I know life would not always be easy but never thought it would be this hard. I have been guessing at my game of life, trying to put my puzzles pieces together. I shout out, "someone, tell me you love me" That's all I wished for in the stars. Life brings me shame. I want to go up and join the stars.

Why am I always so emotional? I cannot control my behavior, it's not clear for me to see what's right. I want someone to stay with me. The grandfather clock strikes loudly in my foyer. Another hour has passed. The sun is beginning to fade. My loneliness comes sooner rather than later. I want to dance with somebody, somebody who loves me, but as the sunset approaches my lonely heart only falls deeper. I know when I breathe, my breath from my lungs makes me feel worthy and wanted. There is only one way I can find peace. If God loves me, he will forgive me. My conscience is struggling again as I am drawn to my medicine on the counter.

I now just want to go to sleep and let my head be gently caressed by my pillow. I crawl into bed in the darkness of my room. I grab my sheets and my blankets. This place, this bed, is what I once shared with my husband. I am drifting off to sleep, I know I will never feel pain again. This emptiness and lost feeling I have inside. I'm falling from the skies without my parachute, plunging to the ground meeting my death. I feel the angels turned their back on me, as my breath slips away. I hear music. I'm going to a place where I've always wanted to be. I silently say to myself my last "Amen."

Chapter 5

Higganum 1959

The weight of my head is embedded into the softness of my pillow. My mind and spirit is lost within a deep unconscious. I am asleep, out cold, from the strong dosage of pills. Sleeping silently, I am lost in a trance dreaming of the past. I travel back to my childhood in Higganum, Connecticut, where I grew up. I can see an image, a figure of me running briskly through the fields with the high green grass touching my knees. The wind is blowing fiercely, forcing my long black hair to slide across my face, partially covering my eyes and nose.

I stop immediately and bend down, extending my arm as I reach for a dandelion that has morphed its yellow crown to white. Using my finger nail, I enjoy breaking, tearing and ripping the strong fibers that compose the green stem. I have separated and severed the shaft from its roots. I look and admire the white, fluffy pompom, the flower of the weed. I can't help but to smile immensely in amusement. Taking a hard deep breath, my lungs expand holding in the pocket of air. I pierce my crinkled lips and with a steady stream, I exhale greatly with force. I watch the fuzzy seeds leave the flower and drift off in the wind, knowing they will find their forever place, imbedded in the dirt, waiting for sunlight to grow its roots. In time I know that these fuzzy little seeds will sprout their beautiful new strong stems as they emerge from the dark soil of the earth.

In this spiritual daydream of mine, I am wearing my long white jumpsuit with bellbottom pants. There is a strong breeze attacking my outfit flapping, folding and bending the extra fabric over in the wind. I feel so insightful and free in this moment.

I never wore or owned that beautiful white jumpsuit created in my dream. I had to hand stitch and sew my own clothes using burlap material from an empty bag of potatoes to make my own shirt. Tiny fingers on my hands sewed every stitch, making sure the small knots held the fabric together. By the end of the day this dry, rough material scratched my skin, causing a red rash with pimples. The burlap was so unbearable and itchy. Children teased me in the classroom with their haunting laughter and jeering comments about my scratchy brown shirt, made me feel worthless. I never received much of anything, so I assumed life wouldn't return much. When you have little, you only expect little. I embraced the premise that you only are as valuable as what life brings you. My worthiness depended on the actions put forth by the people who surrounded me as a child, and who never made me feel important. Although I never verbalized that it was unfair, I struggled to survive engulfed with sadness.

My hand-stitched brown burlap shirt should have been painted black, because I seemed to be the black sheep of the family, the bad seed. I have an older brother, Don and a younger sister Carol. My mother and I had identical names. I'm not sure why, but I guess my parents liked the name Barbara. My mother is a skinny small woman, mean hearted and speaks with a bite in her tongue. My father, Henry, is hard working dad who always wished for another son in the family. To fulfill his void, he never called me Barbara. It was always Bob, as I was considered his second son. Oh how my parents misused and abused the name Bob. "Bob go do this, Bob go do that, Bob did you finish that yet? There is more work to be done Bob. You can't go to bed yet, you need to do this first." The list of chores goes on and on. "Bob, the house is dirty you better clean it and if you don't, I will take you out side in the back and give you lashes with my belt."

On Saturdays mom would send me to the local grocery store to pick up a few items that we could afford. I found some solitude and freedom when I did this chore. I knew I could find peace as I was able to place my tiny feet on the pedals and ride my bike through the fields. When I reached the hills, I could look out and see the wild flowers flaunting their colors of purple and yellow. Among the flowers there were the white puffy, past-flowering dandelions. I could observe their seeds floating and drifting away with the breeze. I savored this time. On my return home with my wire basket completely full, I would stop peddling for a moment and sit still on my bike overlooking the last hilltop. I could see my house far in the distance. My mind is rambling trying to sort through many scenarios. I fear I will be severely punished upon returning. Will there be physical abuse from a mighty hand or fist? Did I do something to misbehave? Will I see any of my mother's wicked behavior? Somehow nothing I do is ever completely right. I have a hard time pleasing my demanding parents.

Growing up in this small town I lived an apartment at the top floor of our duplex on Main Street. I had neighbors living on both sides. One was a Russian man who lived alone. He was a heavy set man who had a thick accent when he spoke. On the other side of our unit lived a family of four from Poland.

I came from a very poor family. My dad was a blue-collar worker and every penny mattered. We sometimes went hungry as my parents often didn't have enough money for food. My father would grab his BB gun from the wall and pass me a fishing net along with a bucket. He would say to me, "It's time to go down to the river behind the house." Then in a serious manner he would say "We are going to catch tonight's dinner, Bob."

My weekly chore became a sequence of action to catch as many frogs as I could. I stored them in my yellow bucket of water with a tight lid on top. This task would be hard at times. Their green, slippery, slimy bodies would hop quickly in the water. I would have to scoop fast with my round circular net to be successful. I could just taste their fried legs in my mouth, the meat tasted just like chicken but a little greasier. As I stalked them in my bare feet, I knew it would take an abundance of frogs to make my hungry belly full. I would be out collecting frogs all day deciding and deciphering along the riverbanks where was the best place to find the hiding croakers. I created and mapped out a routine with my net and bucket ready.

While I caught the frogs, dad was searching for the muskrats. When you come from a poor family, you look for food wherever you can. Dad knew their furry bodies supplied a good bit of meat for the dinner table. My father got ready to shoot while the rats were running for their lives in every direction. He began shooting fast and steady with the pellets hitting the moving targets. I felt sorry for the animals but was just happy and content not to have my stomach growl for the night.

When we returned home my father would say "Bob take the dead muskrats and hang them on the line. Remove their skin with a knife and make them clean, you got that Bob?" Yes I would say. I would have to remove and pick out each BB pellet with the tip of my knife, flinging the pellets to the ground watching them bounce and roll away. During dinner, it was sometimes discovered that I had missed a pellet or two. My parents complained when they bit down hard on a pellet that had eluded my knife.

My responsibilities as a child were never fit for a girl named Barbara. I should have been allowed to wear dainty, pretty dresses, act elegantly and be taken care of. This was not me, I was always Bob, the boy entrapped in his work. I was prohibited from having a normal childhood, unlike my younger sister Carol who never did anything wrong and rarely got disciplined.

Carol was treated like a queen compared to me. She got to go places without being questioned or having to do chores first. My parents, bought her ruffled dresses, tied her hair in bows and made her look exceptionally pretty. A beautiful girl who was treasured and loved. She was allowed her independence, and not forced to stay home and do chores.

I could never understand why I was not allowed the freedom she enjoyed. I was the one given chores with a little beating here and there. As for my brother Don, my parents were astonishingly proud of their only son and loved him dearly. My brother is ten years my senior. Don did help with some light duties around the house, but like Carol, he still was granted his freedom. I only lived my first seven years with my brother in the house. He decided to join the Army at seventeen and never returned back home. When Don left, I was still a young child, and seemed to take over the role of the second son named "Bob".

I could never figure out my life which seemed to me like a delicate, woven spider web, hemming me into a corner. The same spider webs that I whisked away from the nooks and crannies of my house, but not from my mind. I could never understand why I wasn't loved and adored. My siblings never protected me. Even when my parents lashed out at me, they would just walk away. No one stuck up for me. I kept saying to myself that this treatment was unfair and wondered why I was always invisible to my family? I was sure my sister and brother were probably just glad that they weren't the recipients of the lashes or seen as the outcast of the family. As a child you learn to accept. You can adapt, function, and move forward until you become a young adult, then you realize this behavior is vitally wrong.

My father died unexpectedly when I was thirteen years old. He was not as bitter or as mean compared to my mother. He did show me some emotion and affection. I know he cared for me in his own unique way. Right before his death he bought me a sewing machine for my birthday. That was the turning point of my life. I could now mend and make my own clothes stronger and more refined. The refection of my father's sudden death affected our family deeply. My mother was scared about survival, not knowing what she should do. She didn't know how to make money because she was just a housewife. Our family was now even more broken and dysfunctional after we buried my father.

My mother's brother, our uncle George, was nice enough to provide us with shelter. We packed our belongings leaving our small apartment bare, and moved into his home. My mother and sister shared a room together. I was placed in the hallway, no room, no bed, just a pillow and a blanket for sleeping. Of course, I adjusted like I always did. I was just happy to have a roof over my head. I did find peace in this small, narrow hallway. I no longer had to play the role of the unwanted one as my uncle George was good to me. When I turned fifteen he helped me find a job at the local pharmacy down the street. My young history of doing hard work paid off. I finally saved up enough money to move out and become independent. I felt excited and liberated at having my freedom. My new one-bedroom apartment was all mine. It was directly above the pharmacy where I worked, a perfect location for me. I was finally away from my family making my traumatic childhood just a memory and looking forward to my future.

I worked hard and saved up just enough money to buy my first car, a Ford. You can really appreciate freedom when you finally feel you deserve it. My car was not the newest model but these wheels provided me the ability to see more than just this small town of Higganum. Shortly after buying the car, I discovered it was having mechanical problems. My transmission was not shifting right, but I was still able to drive slowly in low gear. I arrived at a local garage called C&I. This is where I met a tall, dark, and handsome man named Innocent. Upon gazing into his beautiful eyes, I wanted him to be my prince. He had such a nice smile and showed me a sincere amount of affection. He let me borrow his personal car while mine was getting repaired. This was, I assumed, to try to win me over. I couldn't believe it, what a nice gesture. I was so amazed by his thoughtfulness.

A week later my car was fixed and ready to be picked up. When I drove back to retrieve my car this handsome prince asked me out on a date. Oh, how I good I felt inside. I was the luckiest woman alive. This tall dark handsome man asking me "Bob" out for a date. I couldn't get the words out fast enough. "Yes," I said replying with a smile. "I would love to go on a date with you." That day the angels were shining down on me. I was the happiest girl alive. I was so lucky to finally meet someone who made me feel so astounding whole. It was wonderful to feel love and worthiness, so unlike the past living in the confines of my broken family.

The first two months flew by. Everything so far was magical. I saw no signs of the temper that was to dominate our relationship. We were so in love—swirling, twirling, hugging and kissing, just like two teenagers running free. We enjoyed our time together immensely while listening to the radio, singing and dancing, creating the life I had wished for.

One extraordinary night under the moon and stars Innocent asked me to marry him. I was so surprised and astonished. A deep sensation of happiness filled my soul. And my heart felt that skipped beat sensation. I found my prince in shining armor. Once again, I couldn't get the words out fast enough, "Yes, yes, I will marry you, I will be your wife!"

A week after the engagement as I was leaving the pharmacy I bumped into John, an old friend. We were talking and catching up about old times in the parking lot. Innocent passed by in his car at the same time. He became outraged that I was talking to another man. He approached us in a jealous state. John decided to leave to avoid a fight. Seconds later, Innocent's behavior went crazy. His nostrils widened and his tempter flared. He was extremely mad and very irrational. He did not want me to be talking to another man, I was his and his only. Innocent applied his fist with all his strength, and punched my windshield creating an impact the size of his fist with spider cracks exploding and destroying my windshield. I witnessed his destructive behavior, extreme force, strength and power. Innocent lost control of himself and was screaming right in my face. I felt his breath brush over me as he shouted. I couldn't escape, not just yet. I was terrified, shocked, and I produced a quick high pitched scream from fright. I could not believe my

The Shattered Oak

knight in shining armor was acting like this as he had
always been so romantic towards me. Why would he
act like this? Will this unreasonable behavior surface
in my future with him?

My close friends at the time advised me not go
through with the marriage and leave him for good. I
guess I should have read the signs, the warning bells
from the angels. I opted not to listen, I chose to turn
my back. I was so in love, my heart still wanted to
carry-on with the marriage.

Innocent apologized the next day for his actions, with a nice bouquet of daisies and sunflowers,
promising he would never raise his voice or show his
anger again. He said he would forever love me and
never use force or hit his wife. His charming personality won my open heart.

A week later, we ran to the Justice of the Peace
to get married. I borrowed my friends white wedding
dress for the ceremony. Innocent and I were standing
together with two witnesses that day. The Justice
speaks, "You are now officially married. May you
both enjoy the rest of your life in peace. You may
now kiss the bride."

This was the day that my whole life changed. I
think Innocent and I were both victims from a past of
childhood abuse and neglect. Our similar back-
grounds connected us on the same level with each
other. We were both forgotten and unworthy as children, making our attraction stronger. Our mutual

dysfunctional childhoods made it easier for us to accept each other. This unique, intertwined connection makes it easier to forgive each other's faults. With our relationship providing us comfort, it isolated us from our common and complex pasts. I tend to look up to those who are superior. I thought I could be rescued from my past, but now I have to be saved from my present.

After we got married, I found out secret information from the past about Innocent. I happened to be putting away clothes in his dresser when I found a piece of paper. It was a marriage certificate from a year ago. Issued from a Justice of the Peace in Virginia. Innocent was married to Betty Jean, on July 21, 1958. I was stunned! I was in too much shock to move, my hands were shaking. I went silent, overwhelmed, barely letting the air out of my lungs, holding my breath. Astonished that my husband never told me about his dirty little secret. What else was he hiding? Why didn't he tell me?

When Innocent came home that night, I confronted him. He denied it at first rambling off a long list of lies. Finally, I found out the truth, he was married for three days. They met while he was in the army. Betty Jean became pregnant and had a baby boy. I began researching all I could about Betty Jean, I found out she annulled her marriage after a few days because Innocent became too violent. Betty Jean didn't want anything to do with Innocent. She left him and stayed with her mother in Virginia. Innocent denies that he fathered a baby boy. He pretended his own son never existed. But, I know the truth. The truth is that my husband can lie. He is not as perfect as I thought.

...

Upon emerging from my daydream, I put the depressing memories of neglect and being unloved out of my mind. In my unconsciousness state I'm off creating a new dream. Although affected by the strong dosage of medicine in the pills, I am drawn to putting my thoughts down on paper. As my tall, skinny BIC pen flows the ink through my fingers to the paper it affords me closure. I write about my experiences in the heavens, my death, my razor blade, my drowning, and my pills. All notes written for God to listen to, or for me to read again and again as a healing tool. The man nailed on the cross is helping me, watching as I expose my thoughts to my notebook. These writings give me salvation. My story is an open book for God to hear and for me to share alone with him. My leather journal with its worn black binder becomes the bible of my life. Scriptures of my past with my own prayers inscribed along the pages are joined with paragraphs of my journey to find my savior, Jesus Christ the Lord.

Chapter 6
Connecticut Institution 1983

Did you ever wonder why some lives become more difficult than others? My life has always been so hard. I am spiritually aware but as my body awakens from unconsciousness and my eyelids begin to open, déjà vu consumes my mind. Bright lights are blaring, hitting my pupils, making them constrict. I'm confused and unfocused wondering where I am. Why is my head feeling so muffled? I strain to focus, staring up at the white ceiling tiles, and bringing my eyes down I see an IV once again in my arm. Doctors and nurses are standing in groups talking quietly in my room.

At the end of my bed, I hear Sara speaking to Isabelle who sounds so stressed. I hear her tell the group, "...almost had an accident, following mom, speeding at 80 miles an hour trying to catch the ambulance." I am having trouble seeing and hearing. I try to concentrate on her broken voice, "Listening to sirens, lights and catching up." I can understand only bits and pieces of the conversation. I am having a difficult time processing what is apparent to me, but I can tell the girls are frightened. My mind can only handle listening and understanding half of what is said. Isabelle says, "Lost sight of the ambulance." The sound waves are vibrating and filtering through my ears, taking their time to sink in. My girls are speaking with a nurse and I can hear them much louder and clearer now. Isabelle utters in sobbing tones, "I can't lose my mother. Please help her." I listen to voices as they express their concern, with my children wondering once again if the hospital is going to save their mother.

The doctors in this emergency department saved my life again, by forcing the charcoal into my body. I vomited again and again and my stomach was pumped as before. I survived my overdose—again! This time my children have no say in what happens to me. The State of Connecticut forces me to go to an institution for my safety. I am not permitted to go home with my girls this time. The doctors fear I would take my life again and succeed. They have me committed to an institution without my permission.

I am now locked up in a caged building, surrounded by the bars on the outside like being in a zoo. Wooden doors and locks with secret codes allow only specific people to get into the area. I walk into the living room area where I see other patients who are the inmates of this institution. I now have to welcome this new sitting area as my home. It resembles and feels like a coffin to me. There is no outside air. It is stifling, suffocating and closed so tightly that it makes it hard to breathe. There is no escape and nobody to hear our screams. We are all buried alive in here. Everything around me is the color of white, the hallways, our rooms and even the small space with the four padded walls for when you misbehave. The walls in my cubicle are white vinyl and although not the silky, white satin padding of a coffin, each of these confines elicit a similar feeling of death. Except in here, there are no beautiful memorial flowers at this funeral site. In this hospital I am under lock and key. No one is able or willing to get me out. The doctors and nurses have access to the outside world. But I am barricaded in behind these locked doors. The staff is determined to keep the crazy folks inside to protect the sane people on the outside.

It's amazing how other people have the power to decide your fate. It's just a doctor's opinion that decides if you're insane. Just a professional opinion scribbled on a piece of paper becomes a file that determines your future. This doctor judges your feelings, your inner soul and charts your status. Do they really know me? How could one person with so little knowledge of who I really am possibly fill out this form? How could they use this paperwork to determine my fate in just twenty-four hours? They have the sole power to decide whether I should return to my home with my three children or be locked up in an institution to be interacting with crazy people. I have no further control to write the rest of this so-called life story. It is so unbearable when other adults make decisions for you against your will. Some decisions may be right, some could be desperately wrong. I am no longer an adult in this institution. I am treated as a child. I am a young girl who had to listen, obey and earn the respect of my surrounding adults or suffer unbearable consequences.

When I was committed to this institution, they stripped me bone naked. I lost all of my rights as an emotional, sane human being. I enjoyed no more personal belongings in my pockets, no hairbrushes in my room, no more objects that I could potentially use to harm myself. They placed me in a white gown with blue tiny flowers, the same style outfit every day with no changes. They feed me drugs to keep me stable and quiet, checking each time underneath my tongue to make sure I take my daily medicine.

This place they call an institution would make a normal person crazy. You are not alive in here. Your spirit and desire for living leaves your body. If you say anything that is defiant, or your actions get out of order, they will have the aides rush to confine you. I have been defensive with my words. I have folded my arms too tightly to my chest. I have not listened when I should have. These are inexcusable and not allowed by this rigid administration.

The staff grabs my arms and legs with their strong hands. They pick me up and place me on a stretcher, quickly applying the nylon straps around my arms and tying them unbearably tight. They place straps around my legs and wrap me up in a strait jacket. These actions restrict most of my breathing and cause me to panic. They swaddle you like a baby.

It's pure torture to have somebody else hold you down. This created a flashback to when my husband would pin me to the bed and force me to have sex.

In my emptiness and aloneness, I feel like I'm going to cry but my tears don't flow. I am trying to fight back against the orderlies but they just fight harder. My kicking and screaming are futile as I never win. My muscles are too small and weak to fight these strong beasts in their white jackets depicting righteous authority. Sometimes, I think the staff finds pleasure in applying straightjackets. I think they could be retaliating for our uncooperative behavior. They wrap and bundle us up like moths in a cocoon.

The staff is around the crazies all day. By living together on the same floor day in and day out this situation could possible put them over the edge. I guess their job isn't easy. This is the time when I miss Alice's couch. The softness of the leather soothed me as I relaxed into that couch, tucked in and secure. I wish I could talk to Alice. She understands me better than the institutional staff who act like wardens in a prison. They only understand prescriptions and how much one should have, balancing every medication and looking for the right fit. Their challenge is to figure out what kind of prescriptions will make me chronically passive, a walking zombie. When my children come to visit, I know they are afraid of my incoherent state. This is something I cannot control. I am completely lethargic and I can barely have an ongoing conversation. All I want to say to my girls is that I miss them, I love them, and I want to go home. The doctors give me such high doses that I am left in a state of drowsiness. All I can do is stare at them with my glossy eyes and with my mouth wide open mumbling words that have no meaning. Side-effects from my medication continually gives me dry mouth making my tongue feel like a wad of cotton. This causes the disfiguring of my words that elicit mumbled sounds. It reinforces an observer's opinion that I am mentally unstable. I know my girls do not like to visit me in this institution, this scary, scary, unimaginable place for the potentially insane.

I feel I'm in a slow, living hell. I don't even like to say that word, but that is the way to describe the atmosphere here. There are patients around you continually screaming in distress while talking repetitively to themselves. A young girl who tried to commit suicide with a pistol blew half of her face off. Bandages are taped alongside her cheek bone to hide her massive wound. Looking at her is so frightening. I can only turn away as there is no escape. I am not allowed to walk out of the common room. I can't even fold my arms to my chest or they will think I'm crazy and defiant. The staff wants all of us to just sit, behave and be still in a controlled environment for twenty four hours a day. I must eat and sleep on their schedule. I am only allowed one hour of television each day. I think we should watch the movie, "One

Flew Over The Cuckoo's Nest" during our sixty minutes of television time. It would be a perfect fit for the audience. I think this is a reality film good for all of the patients to attend.

To get transferred from one building to another we must go through long tunnels. I call them black holes, not expecting an exit. These tunnels are made from concrete and are buried in the ground below the surface of the living space. Square lights on top are the only illumination source. In this dungeon, we are hidden from society and nowhere to be found, just like warriors blindly following our commander-in-chief into an abyss. With no way to escape we are ordered around like troops in the army, complying with the written laws of the institution. You will pay the price if you do not behave.

I do not like to enter these tunnels. They petrify me every time I proceed, causing me to breathe fast and steady in total panic. I can feel the release of air exhaling from my nose with a steady stream, onto my lower lip, while my heart pounds loudly. I usually become sweaty underneath my armpits and moist on my chest. When I enter the tunnel, I repetitively get a bad feeling before I go underneath. I receive a cold chill that shakes my core and enters me without my control. Then quickly, another sensation of claustrophobia sets in like we are all herded cattle going to the slaughterhouse. Except there is no death to look forward to. Our destination is just dull, lifeless and hot like being castaway in a desert.

I shuffle my feet as fast as I can. I still continue to panic and my heart is beating at its fast pace. I hold my breath. My eyes beginning to bulge from the pressure as I refuse to take a blink until I have reached the other end of the tunnel. For now, I am safe from the underground confinement. I have made it to my destination, the main building in this crazy compound for the insane. I climb to the fourth floor, in the tall brick building which has only one window at the end of a hallway. It is a very depressing place. I am a prisoner in this institution and feel as though I'm mentally left in the dark.

There are times, I do enjoy using my imagination. It is in no means a healthy kind of thinking. I see my old oak tree with the woodpecker resting on the crooked branch with its red head matching the color of my angry face. I wish I could use my fingers like a bird's beak. Instead of eating insects, I would peck and swallow up all the people around me. As crazy as it sounds, if my fingers were as sharp as a bird's beak, I could poke their eyes out releasing the fluid, that just like my tears, would trickle down their faces. My anger has risen since I've been captive here, I miss my freedom. Like the woodpecker I long to spread my wings and fan my feathers out for support and guidance. Then I could go wherever I choose and land far away from here. I feel like a tiny bug in this hospital, so vulnerable with no protection even though I keep my emotional shell firmly entrenched. Everyone dictates my life, telling me what to do and what is acceptable. They make me feel unable, incapable and small. Inside these white walls I am nothing but empty flesh, walking around in someone else's skeleton. I don't even miss how I observed life without the sedation drugs, because my memory of reality is so evil and unforgiving.

I also have some soothing dreams in this institution where I climb up to the top of my old dead oak tree that connects me to the castle in the sky. This spot is my tower of safety. I see myself shielded in body armor made of steel, fending off my enemies with a sword. I attack the staff in white coats and trash their clipboards. Inside this castle, I'm drinking holy water from the small white cups. This protects me from my pills, the ones I am forced to take. The dosage they give me is so strong that I am always drowsy. I cannot stay lucid and coherent.

I just want to drink that holy water, helping me to forget this institution and its padded walls. I ask myself, "Is your deep love going to save me God?" My daydream ends, my castle vanishes. For now once again I am not guarded or protected. I am all alone, just me and my white walls.

I do believe some people are definitely meant to be locked up when they are severely mentally challenged. But, I feel my mind is still present. My imprisonment makes me weak in the knees and help-less. I am helpless because I have no choice. Maybe instead of thinking of the woodpecker in my dreams, I should be focused on that long dead, black, charred branch that is hanging off the shattered oak tree. This is the one that extends away from its core entangled with its healthy neighbor's branches. This represents the dead touching the living, producing life. Could this vision give me some hope?

My fantasy daydreams help me survive my sentence here in this institution. Living among the in-sane in here every day gets harder for me. I'm breath-ing, but trying so hard not to drown or cut off the ox-ygen to my limbs. I want to be far away like the pic-ture of the castle in the sky. My daydreams will keep me alive. Where are those large grey stones stacked on top of each other creating my lookout tower high above the clouds? From there I can look out for the enemy approaching. I'm the warrior in armor with all its magical powers of perfection looking down for any unwelcome visitor There is no perfection in this institution, no gate way to heaven through the clouds. There are just tunnels going down, down and down to my medieval cemetery, my final resting place. I can feel the presence of a shallow grave in my bones, so cold and dreary. These white padded walls that confine me make me feel that I am submerged in that grave.

My days have come to an end. The eye of the storm within my hurricane, has come for me. It is my time. I must pay the price for my delusional outbursts. The doctors' order me electric shock therapy. I am horrified upon hearing them usher those harsh directives, drumming death to my soul. I question the reality of my situation. Can this be real? Can somebody pinch me and wake me up? This has to be a nightmare that I am sinking into. Nobody would want to do this to me, would they? A group of nurses and staff members come to collect me. I know I tried to take my own life, but should I have to pay this price? They must be mistaken. It is someone else's fate.

I have a second to think as I am being rolled away. A thought enters my mind. It is a gamble how the number three can be so significant and can play such a role in my life. The three suicide attempts are now in my past. My number three was not a great choice. I now pay the price as I am spread on a table such as Jesus was on the cross. In times of extreme depression I have asked God to help me feel his sacrifice. I prayed to feel his pain before I took my pills. I did hold on to my rosary beads tightly before my past suicide attempt. I guess my wish of feeling his sacrifice has come true. I may not be nailed down to my bed, but my straps are positioned like those on a wooden cross and make me feel like a prisoner. I would have never guessed that my deep prayers to

God would end up with me suffering in a similar fashion.

The staff members strap me down. I am kicking and struggling as the first strap goes on, then another. My legs are still free and I can feel the veins in my arms pulsing, bulging, from distress. I lift my head and my temples are throbbing. I'm screaming on the inside but nobody is listening. Helpless, I pray to God in one last attempt. Will he help me through this? Now I feel the finished touch with both of my legs tightly strapped. I am captured, confined on this wide rolling flat cart. I only can move my eyes to see what is happening around me. Is this how Jesus felt?

I have no feeling in my arms or my legs, just complete numbness. I know where they are taking me and what leads down this hallway—to that special room. That room that only the crazy, mixed up minds go. That room where the sign on the door says High Voltage, Danger! Like my husband who I could not escape, now I cannot escape my fate decided upon by the institution's staff. I have to be dreaming. Please God say it is not so. This has got to be a very bad dream and I will soon awaken from my horror. I need to feel my rosary beads in my palm, my Savior. Where are they? Why have they taken away my precious piece of hope and salvation. Why God? Why do I deserve this continuation of torture linked to my state of helplessness. Why do these "wardens" have the right to decide to shock me? Why do they have the right to strap me up? Why are they allowed to hook me up, wire after wire all over my brain and on my chest to monitor my heart? Will this remove my sense of self after this?

My emotions are running wild. Do they have the right to send voltage through me making my muscles twitch and convulse? I am feeling like I'm about to walk through a thunderstorm with volts hitting my body like lightning. The contents of my stomach will wretch as they keep repeating the procedure over and over, again, trying to trigger my mind to resume their definition of sanity.

With my execution about to start, I pray one more time loudly in my mind. I am imagining I have my rosary in my hand, feeling the invisible cross. I pray that the limbs on my body won't detach like that broken branch of the old oak tree after getting struck by lightning. The electric charge will traumatize every living cell. I feel as if I will be dead at the core, sapping all of the energy from me. The current will fry the hairs on my skin producing that burnt body odor. Can this procedure find out what is the matter with me? One doctor orders for the proceeding to start and begin the shocking at once. The countdown begins one, two, three. The voltage starts, and my cries are unheard. Wires with their voltage pulsing through my skin, running through my mind, going down my spine. It passes the lower half of my body and out through my toes.

I hear the doctors talking loudly. They assess my behavior and my vital signs. They adjust the current as they see fit. Part of me has been left behind forever within this high-voltage room. I have no more rights or freedom. I am stripped naked at the core. I did not die of convulsions or seizures. I am shaken and rattled, but I am also strong and resilient. God has saved me once again and I emerged alive from my treatment. I decided to fight with all my might to survive my hideous journey within the confines of this institution.

My routine changes after that night and I start to get a little smarter. I try to win my battle on my own. I become wiser and find a way to hide my pills in my mouth. I make a pocket, a crevice, folding the pill in the corner of the back of my tongue. I open my mouth for inspection, but keep my secret pouch to myself. I start to feel the change. I can feel myself thinking, and talking much clearer.

I noticed a certain nurse having a special interest in me, while watching my moves and my motions. She listens to me speak, really hears me, and understands my thinking. She is always evaluating me in a positive way. She schedules meetings to meet with doctors and my daughters about my wellbeing.

This is the same nurse that was in my room when I was changing my gown. She noticed the dark purple wide stretchmarks on my breast. She was really surprised to see such an unusual color. She noticed the markings were on my belly as well. She approached me and softly touched my midsection swaying her fingers tips following along the purple trail of marks. She walks around my naked body and asked how I got so many bruises on my arms and legs. I really didn't have too much of an answer for her, so I shrugged my shoulders. She made a comment about my puffy neck and shoulders. She told me to go ahead and put on my clean new gown.

I noticed she was evaluating me in a positive way as she reaches for the wall phone in my room. She begins talking to another staff member as I am listening to their conversation. My nurse is speaking really intensely when she voices her opinion about some article she had just read last week. She is rambling on about a list of symptoms and requests to set up a meeting with my doctor. Before she hangs up, she initiates a second request and asks whoever is on the phone to find the name and phone number of the family member listed on my chart. Her last words on the phone were that she needed to discuss with my family information about my wellbeing.

Being on strong medicine puts me in a semi-coherent state, so I never was able to think of how my daughters have really felt. Now that I have been hiding my pills, I am remembering the past and interpreting memories in a more lucid state. I realized that Isabelle, as a young adult, received the brunt of having to take responsibility for me while I was here. She had to handle all the sessions with the doctors and authorize decisions about my care in this facility. Appointment after appointment, she took the time to care for my safety and wellbeing. She became the responsible one and tended to the house while I was mentally sick. Isabelle at the age of eighteen, playing the part of mom, became the legal guardian of her younger sister. Isabelle took custody of her, so the State would allow Sara to stay in the house. This was such a tremendous responsibility for a young girl who earlier had her own dreams of going to law school. Assuming the role of mother prevented her from fulfilling her goals, for now.

My other daughter Mary, at the age of nineteen, moved out of the house and got an apartment with her boyfriend. She wanted to get away from the madness of our unstable home. Innocent did not want to take on the responsibility of the girls, but he always mailed a weekly check for my two daughters. My family now is divided, split apart because of a broken mother.

Nancy, the nurse who befriended me, is an angel in my eyes. She came and rescued me. I am so grateful she took the time to notice I was different. Nancy concluded that I was not crazy like the others. I do believe that we encounter certain people for a reason during our lifetime. She noticed signs and symptoms of Cushing's disease. This is a disease that over secretes the Adrenocorticotropic hormone

(ACTH), over-stimulating the adrenal glands' cortisol production. Today, cortisol is now known as the stress hormone that is produced in your adrenal glands located above your kidneys. This overstimulation can cause you to become severely depressed and moody, symptoms that I chronically deal with. This information was not available when I was in the sanitarium.

She discussed the disease with my doctors, explaining to them it is a new disease undergoing further research and this discovery is vital. She told them about my swollen moon shaped face, puffy shoulders, purple stretchmarks on my breasts, bruise marks on my body and swollen belly. She fought my case with the doctors and won my freedom. The doctors ordered a cortisol test that measures the level of hormones in my blood, urine and saliva. The test results would show if my levels were too high or too low. And if they were off that meant that I have a disorder in my adrenal glands. These disorders can be serious if not treated. Within a few days my test results came in. My levels of cortisol were extremely high.

Nancy opened the door allowing me to be released from the black iron bars of this institution. When my transfer was complete I felt there was a light shining around me. An angel is saying, "take my hand and I will spread my wings. There is nothing we cannot do together." I felt this message in my soul. I could feel the light of warmth surround me making my body temperature rise. I will be in an ambulance tomorrow morning and on my way to the National Institute of Health in Bethesda, Maryland, which is a unique medical center devoted entirely to clinical research. It is a scientific hospital where they study new diseases with hopes to find treatments and cures.

So many words describe my dark days in this institution. If only these walls could talk so the other patients could hear ways to win their cases. Although many great things may take place in this hospital to try and cure the crazy mind, I always knew this wasn't where I belonged. I am grateful to be leaving this institution. My body and soul are uplifted. I am relieved to escape from all the horrors that were inflicted on me. Thanks to Nancy I was protected when I was weak. She returned my freedom, as my knight in shining armor. She may be the savior in my picture— that gold frame that holds the castle in the sky. Nancy and God have saved me from my ordeal. These iron walls are going to be lifted. I will be free from my extraordinary mixed up past.

It is my last night lying in this hospital bed. My grief will be over soon. I muse over my history. It's unbelievable what trauma from stress can do to your body and health. The daily turmoil destroyed my wellbeing, took its toll, and produced extremely high levels of cortisol. It is astonishing how the past can affect the present. I now know I need to get rid of my stressors. I need to find peace, and lower my cortisol levels in order to heal my broken body.

I am looking forward for my new journey at NIH hospital. My path in life has forever changed the way I live. My mind has been blindsided and I am still a long way from home. I can only pray my discovery of Cushing's disease will cure my suffering and release that emotional pain that is still present within my mind.

Chapter 7

Bethesda Maryland

My year-long incarceration in the institution is forever behind me. I have decided to file that chapter away in my soul. I am so grateful that part of my life is now in the past, but I know it will always be a piece of me. I do have some hurdles to jump over and I am not completely running away from my past. I do still carry my own burdens and pain. It's what I make of them that matters. I have been broken in many ways, but I am still strong, and my life will go on.

Often our paths in life are chosen for us even though they may not be pleasant. My passage may be ultimately up to God, but after all my sacrifices I will be able to move forward choosing to cope with my battle scars. I will take my disadvantages head on. Just like the horns of an ox or the fist of my husband, I will plow right through the grassy fields from my childhood. My life represents two forces that bonds me together—a positive and a negative, equivalent to my electric shocks. I am determined to put positive energy in my thoughts in hopes of creating a stronger, happier, mentally sound mind. Negative thinking only wears me down when I focus on the past feelings of depression. I will build my spirit strong and only think positive thoughts. I have learned a lot through this ordeal.

Valuable knowledge can be extracted from our past by absorbing our mistakes along the way. Life is meant to grasp our experiences, learning how our impressions can change us for the positive after living through our heartaches and burdens that transform our future into proud accomplishments. My success will help me to embrace my own worthiness. After finally accepting that the past is a path we choose not to repeat, we can watch ourselves grow inside like a seed, creating a new life. I have learned that I have the capability to make my own choices in life. It's how I elect to see, digest, and live my life that matters. I will persevere by looking within to understand and respect myself, to find my clever spirit along the way with my inner peace.

I am yet again returning to another hospital with white coats, doctors and nurses. This tall brick building has the appearance of a very professional operation with experienced, promising, and brilliant physicians. There are no guards and no enclosures to prevent my escape. I have faith that they will cure my embroiled mind during my time as a subject during their clinical research trials. I have faith in God that my thoughts will become pristine and clear while I am here. I have been informed of their theory of how I developed Cushing's disease. It manifested because my cortisol levels remained extremely high. The doctors tell me this can happen when one suffers trauma with high amounts of stress. Typical of my body's response to the abuse I suffered in the past, I now know that my struggles from childhood carried into my marriage and now they are affecting me in the present. Everyone has a past that can cause them to reflect on who they really are. The vision I hold of myself is complicated. And there is a deeper, deranged and more destructive past ever present in my subconscious.

Cushing's disease has many common signs and symptoms that make it hard to identify the disease. Numerous patients get misdiagnosed. I was one of the lucky ones who was transferred to the National Institute of Health. I am so grateful this hospital has the funding for my clinical trial and that they are gathering knowledge that may cure my dysfunctional mind.

During my ambulance ride to the hospital I was frightened for what was to come and apprehensive about being another patient in another hospital far away from home. As the ambulance doors begin to open, I can feel my anxiety, and aloneness dominating my spirit. My senses heighten from the apprehension. I intensely miss my long rosary necklace which could soothe me. This cross with its red, ruby beads linked together with a gold clasp, could provide me significant amount of comfort and peace now. All I can do for now is just visualize this welcome and comforting vision.

The staff members greet my parked ambulance at the back door of the hospital. I am unloaded, wheeled, and moved to the inside of the building. Once again placed and pushed on a rolling cart. My upper body exposed with my arms displayed on the outside touching the warm white blankets beneath. The oxygen mask is still covering my face, supplying only fresh air into my lungs which reduces the chance of a panic attack. The staff members dressed in their long white coats proceed to roll me down a hallway to the elevator. The light on the elevator panel illuminates for the eighth floor and off I roll into the hallway. I watch the numbers proceed as they are taking me up to my destination.

The elevator doors open, and I continue down a light-yellow painted hallway passing the nurse's station. As I begin to advance closer to my room. I receive many welcoming greetings from the nurses that are behind the desk. Lifting my head, I look at the walls around me. Light is glaring, shining, and bouncing from the reflection of the large hanging pictures. Placing my tired head back down I stare up at the ceiling. Signs are attached with extra bold, black letters, reading East, West, or arrows pointing to a separate wing. I create an image in my mind seeing my castle in the sky offering protection. I could just picture its gold etched frame hanging, guarding these metal doors and walls. My thoughts of daydreaming have followed me here. Now I know I am secure, safe and not alone. The staff turns my rolling cart into my room, number 3041.

The new staff here is very welcoming with their smiles and gentle touches. They use the sheets from under my body to transfer me and place me on my new bed. As my body sinks into the mattress I can see the chrome railings and the remote control that adjusts the bed. Near me on the night stand there is a bottle of water and a folder in bold red letters, reading NIH hospital. As I enter the room, a nurse takes my oxygen mask off. I am so relieved to have this clear plastic shield removed relinquishing my connection to any machinery. I begin to smell a clean faint scent of bleach in the air which reminds me of my Spic and Span house. The daytime nurse introduces herself as Stacey. She is very inquisitive trying to fill in the blanks about my condition, investigating my case and checking my vital signs.

Looking at walls painted light blue, I proceed to admire my surroundings. I am calmed by this shade of blue. Stacey uses her black ink marker on the white board, charting my transfer with red lines permanently separating the information. She adds the date, time, and my vital signs. This large white board is attached to a plain blue wall which is a welcome change from the white vinyl padded walls that surrounded me in the institution. The feeling of being human again envelops and consumes my soul. After Stacey leaves and I open my folder which was left on my side table. In one pocket there is a lunch menu, and in the other pocket is a TV directory. I look up to scan the room. I notice the television fastened to the wall near the long dark blue curtains cascading to the floor. Out of my tall window I can see the narrow view of another roof top with shingles.

On the wall to my left is a large picture of a long wooden pier with a grass hut directly at the end overlooking the blue ocean. Is this a vacation spot or a tropical island paradise depicting where I am? Will I be able to relax and enjoy my stay in this room? What a stunning, breathtaking and opposite environment from the institution. I feel more joyful and at peace and content with my surroundings.

NIH hospital is what I call a little slice of heaven, carved out just for me. By researching my disease, doctors will try to find a cure and to make my illness disappear. I will have no medical bills after my time spent in this hospital. There is always a price to pay though, even when it's free. Nothing is ever completely free, and shortly I find out what is required of me. I am used as a human experiment for daily findings and recordings. The world is just finding out about Cushing's disease and if it can be treated successfully. All the patients on my floor have the same illness. Some have different variations and forms of the disease with different problems and different prognosis. The study should be comprehensive and hopefully a cure will be found for all of us.

My body is charted and experimented with every day. Vials of blood are drawn from my skinny arms; my veins bruised from the injection sites. I am pricked by sharp needles inserted in my skin leaving red dots as markers. A thorough procedure including charting and daily testing is a must. It is mentally challenging to be a guinea pig. I am a rat in a box, or a gerbil running in circles on a wheel. My mind is spinning like those vinyl records playing on my stereo. I am trying to find the right song while listening to the music, but I am not singing any tunes. I receive my extra small white cup along with my new prescription of pills and down them gingerly. I am then evaluated for any new symptoms or unusual behavior. I am a walking, talking test tube –a science project. I'm a human lab experiment while they try to find the right compounds to cure my existing devastating disease.

I am about to endure a full MRI scan that will produce images of my brain. I am placed on a machine which slides inside a white tunnel and told not to move. Flashbacks surge through my mind as I proceed into the mechanical tunnel. My body grows stiff and cold as they slowly roll me through. Visions are running out of control in my mind—darkness, fear, suffocation, loneness. I can feel my past, tightening, strapping, silencing me. When will I see the light? Will I see the light from God? Or will I continue to see any light? Please let me escape this tunnel.

My stomach goes sick, nauseous, twisting and aching with a dull pain. My fear consumes me. I am frightened and scared. I must stay still for five long minutes during my scan. I hear the machine rolling under me, I am finally moving forward escaping the tunnel of entrapment. I will never like the feeling of tunnels that to me are like walls of separation that keeping me isolated from the outside, removing me from life. This is a very familiar memory that expands and seeps slowly from my wounds, ultimately finding a way out. I take a deep, calming breath and utter a sigh of relief. I made it out of this MRI without succumbing to the fear. My inner strength has conquered the claustrophobia that surrounded me.

The doctor reviewed my tests from the imagery. They found a microscopic tumor in my brain. It is located on my pituitary gland that has the power to control a considerable amount of my body's functions. Symptoms related to this tiny tumor can cause erratic emotions and severe depression. He begins talking about a procedure where the neurosurgeon will bypass the brain tissue to get to the tumor by going through the nasal passage. The risk for neurologic complications with this technique is very low, and the surgery leaves no visible scar. I was trying to concentrate while the doctors were explaining to me, but my head was in a fog. Trying to comprehend all this information caused my mind to go blank. My thoughts are acting as though they were in a tin can sealed shut and placed in the dark. I was able to open the lid slowly to hear one detail at a time, taking time to process the word, tumor. My sadness awaits, knowing I need surgery. I am all alone in these decisions and have to continue my path of trusting my doctors.

The anesthesiologist gives me a drug to put me to sleep and I wait for my daydreams to come. The neurosurgeon is trying this new procedure on me during the operation. The video cameras are placed strategically around my bed, recording every angle to capture this medical procedure. The video captures the tools and instruments used in my operation, with the surgeon explaining in detail about my operation. This will be an instructional film describing what to insert and how to cut the tumor. It is designed for the resident doctors in order to learn and duplicate what these highly-skilled surgeons perform using a scope as their tool.

They begin to enter the socket of my nose with their device. Maneuvering this instrument behind my nose canal to reach my pituitary gland and sever off my tumor. The surgery is quite extensive. As the neurosurgeon talks his way through my surgery it is recorded by the cameras. My tumor is removed, and my surgery is finished. They use extra gauze and pack my nose full to prevent any excess blood and future bleeding.

Hours after surgery I awaken slowly from the anesthesia. I have a horrible feeling in my nose and I cannot breathe. I have to inhale and exhale out of my mouth. I can feel the pressure from the gauze. For the next couple of days I have many sleepless nights, but taking my pain medicine helps me recover and shortly my appetite returns. The worst part following my surgery was when the doctors decided to remove the packing from my nose. The gauze just keeps coming out of my nostrils, piece by piece. I could feel every strip sliding slowly across my nose hairs and skin. One long strip after another with spots of dried brown blood on the white gauze. This was the most exasperating part of my experience of the surgery and tremendously painful.

Days after my surgery the doctors issued one more MRI test on my pituitary gland. The film images concluded that the tumor was completely removed from my brain. An empty space was left in the cavity with the slides of the x-ray showing a huge hole where the tumor was extracted. The surgeons had to remove an extra mass of tissue as a safety measure to insure they got every cell of the growing tumor.

Months after my surgery, my results were exceptionally promising and my ordeal with Cushing's disease has come to a final chapter. I was so happy to end this nightmare of being a subject in a clinical trial. I'm so very grateful to NIH, but also ecstatic to be free from the poking, prodding and being a medical experiment.

The day has come for my release, my hospital walls are evaporating. This clinical study has learned all that it could and are now finished analyzing my body. My testing, probing and investigation is now over. I can now stand with my two feet firmly on the ground having a stable mind and a feeling of superior wellbeing. Doctors sign my documents and I am free, with no more locked doors, something I have been waiting so patiently for. My daughters arrive, I can see them walking in my room door. Room number 3041 will just be another memory added to my history.

I am ready to leave feeling revived and in good spirits. With my tumor out, I should have few side effects. My hormones will be out of whack for a while, but I will be leaving this hospital along with a low dose prescription. The medicine is for controlling my hormones not for psychiatric reasons. I will have yearly follow-up appointments and after that I will be free and clear from my disease. I am released from depression and should be back to normal within a year.

I'm not sure what the next thirty years will hold, but for now I have unlocked all my private secluded doors and put them behind me. I have been set free from my nervous breakdown and depression. Learning now that I was not the one who was mixed up broken and insane, but ultimately it was attributed to my Cushing's disease.

Chapter 8

The Long Way Home

Driving up my driveway for the first time in two years brings out an intense, heartbreaking and very emotional feeling. Sadness envelopes me regretting the time gone by. I have to stop and rest for a moment. I want to take in the beautiful landscape that surrounds my home. The last few years I only had memories—an image of my house tucked away in my mind. No more daydreaming as all my visions are now manifesting but are in the present. I am frozen, motionless and stiff, not wanting this view of my home to ever disappear again. So much has changed since the last time I drove up this gravel driveway.

Looking towards my old oak tree, I see it is now completely broken at the bottom of the base where it separated at the trunk. Its big massive trunk lying down on its side, touching the ground with branches twisted in a heap creating a shadow underneath. All I can see is jagged knife-like edges sprouting from its base. I cannot help but be overwhelmingly sad because of my significant connection that tree. This once proud oak has so many stories emanating from its core, extending out making their way through its crooked branches. It must feel a similar pain like the arthritis in my hands branching out to each of my fingers, reacting to the cold, damp weather. The tree has been compromised leaving its shattered soul for Mother Nature to destroy and decay. Age is catching up with me as well. I am worn out and drained. I know one day my time will come too, I will fall down like the tree and lose my beating heart. I will be lifeless at the core just like my favorite oak, my knight in shining armor. But for now my heart still beats loudly in the cavity of my chest one beat at a time.

I get a phone call from my brother, Don after only being home for a month. It's a sad phone call, letting me know he is passing away from cancer. He says he wants to clarify some things that happened in our childhood to explain and justify what he never had the courage to tell me. He asks if I remember our Russian neighbor, Keith who lived on the right side of our duplex. I do remember his face and his voice. He spoke broken English but mostly communicated in Russian. Don starts telling me his story about how the Russian neighbor had an affair with our mom. I was dumbfounded staring at the phone in disbelief. He delivers the even more shocking news that mom got pregnant and had his baby. I am imagining my mother embracing the neighbor and not my father. My brother's story feels completely insane. Then the most shocking part Don says fast, "You are that baby and dad found out." My mind explodes, spinning around, and around like my vinyl records going backwards. This is why I was so rotten at the core. I was a bastard child at birth. I see my life flashing before my eyes. It's all making sense. The earth is moving under my feet. My heart is feeling pressure like the needle that I jabbed into my Kodak photo of Innocent. Within the core of my body I can feel pain similar to the wood fibers, sprouted, jagged and broken like tiny knives in the base of the broken oak tree. This is the same feeling I used to get when Innocent directed his verbal shards during his violent outbreaks. I've suffered so much abuse and so many bruises. This unwelcome news tore at my heart.

I have snapped again. Pieces of my soul leave through my tears that are rolling rapid like a raging river cascading down my face. Teardrops that sound like hail as they fall from my cheeks to the floor. I have encountered a hurricane, embraced by a tornado, a twister of evil meeting me head on with gale force winds. I can see eye to eye in this strangling, forceful, damaging storm which upgraded its energy and mangled the roots of my soul. I realize why I was never loved. I was this misfit that nobody wanted to adore, embrace or hold.

The effects of this news will forever carve a deep scar in my soul and I fear it could return me to my depressive state. My subconscious enters a deep, dark, tunnel that keeps traveling down and down. There is no final point to reach. The scar in my soul has no limits. Now I know where I fit in. I know why the heavens have rained down on me. A dark angel must have come to me at birth with a gray haze, enveloping the sky above, seeding my DNA with that of the Russian neighbor. I may not feel proud to be a bastard child, but I am now in touch with my childhood. My life makes perfect sense to me now. This devastating news eventually sets my mind at ease.

I finally accept my lineage and the next day I called a tree service. I wanted closure to my life and somehow, I knew where I could find it. It is hidden in both of our cores—mine and that of the dead old oak tree. The following day a man came to my home with his chainsaw. The hand equipment starts and the blade goes in. I hear the loud, rough and vibrant sound. My heart sinks with great sadness at this moment when he cuts the tree carcass down to the surface of the ground, completely severing its core at its base. Sawdust flows like a water spout, spraying across the yard like ashes thrown on a grave. If I could, I would hug that invisible old oak tree one more time. But for now, I will have to say my goodbyes by watching quietly in amazement.

I admired that oak in my yard. It has been my life line, my true love. I found beauty and freedom within the strong branches of its solitary and individuality. To look at our surroundings and enjoy the beauty of nature can we open ourselves to the magnificence of life being so timeless? I commit to enjoying every last minute that I have on this precious earth. I know my life has not been perfect. Somehow, I will absorb the healing vibrations of the blue sky and the rays of sun shining in on me. I will find the inner strength to envelop my soul and free me from depression. I realize laughter and smiles can get you through your darkest days. Most importantly I am so grateful to be me. Gratitude reminds me to see the future with courage. I have survived and found peace and serenity with God. This positive attitude shall deliver me warmth and love, something that has been missing until now. My grief and the scars of my past will fade, leaving me a new future to face.

I have learned much through this ordeal and have mapped a path for following a more positive life. Thoughts are like looking at our reflection in the water—glimmering, smeared, blurred and even upside down—sometimes effecting our minds to the brink of insanity. I will choose to control my thoughts without wavering to painful distractions. My vision needs to stay clear and only reflect on what is important. I cannot not focus on the negative. I have accepted my past and choose not to hold onto any grudges. I would not be who I am today without the dysfunctionality of my life. Nor would I appreciate my inner fears or utilize my dependence on others without the struggles that have consumed my life.

The years that have taken their toll have also made me a unique individual, giving me a blessing every day and instilling in me the courage to move on. I am now more independent and resilient with my insecurities waning. I just needed time to make things right, forgive and understand why some people act the way they do. Our behavior may stem from our upbringing or the environment we grew up in. Sometimes the path we choose can distance ourselves from the choices we have made in the past. I try and understand what drives some people to irrational thinking that unleashes hate. I choose not to feel sorry for myself and seek forgiveness. This sets my mind free.

As I grow older, I have chosen to live my life in solitude, having few friends. Nature becomes my solace and true companion. I find serenity by taking long walks in the woods, holding my sickle like a golf club swinging it back and forth cutting the long grass as I walk. Trimming the shards of hay reminds me of the fields in Higginum, while working in my yard fulfills my state of peace. Some people don't find enjoyment in hard labor, but for me it's comforting because it's all I knew as a child. Hard work is in my DNA. This is the medicine that cures my mind and heals my body. This house that was once a house of horrors is now my cathedral, my savior with a single stain glass window placed up high above the rafters of my living room.

It is almost December the time we celebrate Jesus Christ our Lord. Oh how I love the holidays in my home. This year I decide to buy a live Christmas tree. The fun of placing the ornaments on the wide pine branches and draping tinsel to shine some light, is an experience that eluded me as a child. I never got to celebrate any holidays or find the true spirit of Christmas when I was young. Now I cherish the season and decorate my house in splendor. I now feel love and comfort with my children and cherish this time in my beautiful home with my Savior, the Lord.

Daydreams still stay with me even in my senior years. Emotions from my dead oak still run wild when I am driving in my car. I scan the roads and highway looking out to see the vastness of the trees despairing at those that have met their demise through storms or disease. They are hidden among the healthy and the living. They stand out as sorrowful icons with no leaves, just bare. I get a weird sensation when I stare at their nakedness. I do not think of them as disfigured, ugly and broken, or unresponsive. I perceive their bareness in a different way. I know they may be considered an eyesore. Some trees may only have a few dried-up brown leaves left hanging by a thread, but I know they have been through tough times with Mother Nature, strong and wise beyond their years. I can see their beauty shining out from their core, as they extend a branch for one of us to embrace and hold. Their coloring matches that of a grey knight in shining armor, reaching up protecting the sky and the angels.

I think we should all value what we see when we pass an undernourished tree. Spend a few moments, admire and notice them among the living along our roadways. Don't think of them as broken and abused, but as trees who accomplished their journey in life, grateful and connected to nature. When we see these trees it is a reminder prompting us to help the weak. Like the intertwined roots of the healthy trees trying to nourish the dying from below, it symbolizes our need to help others less fortunate. Let's not forget the forgotten.

It's been years since I have grabbed my blue BIC pen and placed my thoughts on my note pad with light blue lines going in one direction. I relate this to the passing of time as we are always moving forward. When I write, my body is physically in the room, but I am emotionally absent. I cannot hear my surroundings as writing consumes, enchants and mesmerizes me. It takes me away from the present and brings me to a place of peace, guiding my mind and spirit bringing out the best in me. I acknowledge the fact that I want to find myself again and immortalize my life in a book for some to read as inspiration, and for the injured to discuss their darkest days. I want to share my pain and loneliness, to help and pray for those who feel weak. Through my words, I may help them cope and achieve their survival. Maybe my thoughts will help them to find their inner strength and muster the courage to find professional help. As I write my life in this leather journal, I hope others can find salvation and peace. I reach for my pen placed in the cup holder on the desk. I press down seeking for my first blue line on the page. I open my mind and release my thoughts. The wounds of my soul are spilling out onto my paper. My pen begins to release the blue ink, writing a story that needs to be told. Amen.

Post Script

Barbara was a wonderful loving mother. Life may not have always been easy, but you gave your family the gift of strength. Some would say that you were an angel sent down from heaven, to see what one person can handle during hardships in life. You are a kind, sweet angel who never deserved all the tortures that you experienced. It's sad to see a broken heart, when one could be so vivid and immensely brave. Barbara you have lived to the beat of your own heart. This is what survival can do in such unbearable conditions.

I hope you as a reader can beat to your own heart and survive your own life's journey. Some would say there is strength in numbers. Reach out to those who you love and provide comfort and protection. Seek shelter with friends if you are struggling from spousal abuse. Fear alone can take from one's innocence. Fearful of your next attack can weaken your soul.

Some stories are meant to be a secret and some stories are meant to be forgotten. Some stories need to be heard to help the survivor live.

There is help for women battling domestic violence, child abuse, suicide, and Cushing's disease. Please see the links below for further information. My love goes out to all the strong women. May you find comfort and peace in your voice that must be heard. May your prayers and your strength heal your life's misfortunes.

...

On the very day we were doing our final edits before going to press, Barbara passed away. Her soul now is free as she runs in the meadow and swings from her old oak tree. Her final amen, years after her recovery, has lifted her spirit to the heavens.

Resources

Domestic Violence: Hot line 1-800-799-7233

Child Abuse: Hot line 1-800- 4-A-Child
(1-800-422-4453) www.childhelp.org

National Suicide Prevention Lifeline:
1-800-273-8255

You are in crisis, reach out for help. Text REASON
to 741741 www.crisistextline.org

Thursday's Child:1-800 USA KIDS
(1-800-872-5437) www.thursdayschild.org

Cushing's disease: www.Cushings-Help.com and
www.Cushings-Support.com

Other Books by Safe Goods

The River's Bend	$ 18.99
A Barnstormer Aviator	$ 12.95
Flying Above the Glass Ceiling	$ 14.95
Spirit & Creator (Spirit of St. Louis)	$ 29.95
Letters from My Son	$ 22.95
Nutritional Leverage for Great Golf	$ 9.95
Overcoming Senior Moments Expanded	$ 9.95
Prevent Cancer, Strokes, Heart Attacks	$ 11.95
Cancer Disarmed Expanded	$ 7.95
Eye Care Naturally	$ 8.95
Aaargh! Menopause	$ 9.95
Live Longer with Cellular Rejuvenation	$ 9.95
Think and Feel Younger	$ 9.95

www.SafeGoodsPublishing.com

Printed and bound by PG in the USA